V l₇ l₇·00.

55p

D0525922

REVISION EXAMPLES IN MATHEMATICS

metric edition

By the same author

Calculus and Co-ordinate Geometry
Differential Equations for Sixth Forms
Revision Examples in Algebra
Revision Examples in Arithmetic
Revision Examples in Geometry
Examples in Trigonometry
A First Geometry
Arithmetic
'O' Level Geometry
Examples in C.S.E. Mathematics
Examples in Modern Mathematics
Examples in Statistics

REVISION EXAMPLES

IN

MATHEMATICS

metric edition

R. L. BOLT, M.Sc.

Senior Mathematics Master,
Woodhouse Grove School

J. M. DENT & SONS LTD
BEDFORD STREET, LONDON, W.C.2

© J. M. Dent & Sons Ltd, 1966

Made in Great Britain
at the
Aldine Press · Letchworth · Herts
for
J. M. DENT & SONS LTD
Aldine House · Bedford Street · London

First published 1966
Reprinted 1967
Second edition 1970
Reprinted 1971
Reprinted 1973

ISBN 0 460 09454 8

PREFACE

THIS book has been designed for use during revision for G.C.E. papers based on the 'Alternative' syllabus. It is hoped that it will also prove useful for other examinations of a similar standard.

Particular attention has been given to the needs of weaker pupils by providing easy graded examples at the beginning of many exercises; these are designed to revise ideas and processes and to lead to the later questions of examination standard. These later questions have been modelled on those set in recent examination papers.

Each of the five Test Papers at the end of the book contains three questions of 'Section A' type and three of 'Section B' type, and should take about one and a half hours to complete.

R. L. B.

NEW EDITION

BRITISH units have been replaced by SI metric units; shillings and pence by new pence.

R. L. B.

CONTENTS

DATA AND FORMULAE

1 millimetre (mm)	$= \frac{1}{1000}$ metre (m)
1 centimetre (cm)	$= \frac{1}{100}$ metre
1 kilometre (km)	$= 1000$ metres

1 kilogramme (kg)	$= 1000$ grammes
1 metric tonne (t)	$= 1000$ kilogrammes

1 are (a)	$= 100$ square metres (m²)
1 hectare (ha)	$= 100$ ares
1 square kilometre (km²)	$= 100$ hectares

1 litre (l)	$= 1000$ cubic centimetres (cm³)

$$\text{Speed} = \frac{\text{Distance}}{\text{Time}}, \ \text{Distance} = \text{Speed} \times \text{Time}, \ \text{Time} = \frac{\text{Distance}}{\text{Speed}}$$

$$\text{Gain (or loss) per cent} = \frac{\text{Gain (or loss)}}{\text{Cost price}} \times 100$$

Simple Interest formula: $\quad I = \dfrac{PRT}{100}$

Circle	Circumference: πd or $2\pi r$	Area: πr^2
Parallelogram	Area:	base $\times$ height
Triangle	Area:	$\frac{1}{2}$ base $\times$ height
		$\frac{1}{2} bc \sin A$
		$\sqrt{s(s-a)(s-b)(s-c)}$
Trapezium	Area:	$\frac{1}{2}(a+b)h$
Prism	Volume:	(area of base) $\times$ height
Pyramid	Volume:	$\frac{1}{3}$(area of base) $\times$ height

Cylinder

Curved surface area: $2\pi rh$ Volume: $\pi r^2 h$

Cone

Curved surface area: πrl Volume: $\frac{1}{3}\pi r^2 h$

Sphere Surface area: $4\pi r^2$ Volume: $\frac{4}{3}\pi r^3$

$\pi \simeq 3\frac{1}{7}$ or 3.1416

Identities. $(a + b)(c + d) = ac + ad + bc + bd$
$$(a + b)^2 = a^2 + 2ab + b^2$$
$$(a - b)^2 = a^2 - 2ab + b^2$$
$$(a + b)(a - b) = a^2 - b^2$$

Quadratic Equation. $ax^2 + bx + c = 0$ has solutions
$$x = \frac{-b \pm \sqrt{b^2 - 4ac}}{2a}$$

Indices. $a^x \times a^y = a^{x+y}, \quad a^x \div a^y = a^{x-y}, \quad (a^x)^y = a^{xy}$

$a^0 = 1, \quad a^{\frac{1}{q}} = \sqrt[q]{a}, \quad a^{\frac{p}{q}} = \sqrt[q]{(a^p)}$ or $(\sqrt[q]{a})^p$

$a^{-x} = \dfrac{1}{a^x}, \quad \left(\dfrac{a}{b}\right)^{-x} = \left(\dfrac{b}{a}\right)^x$

Differentiation. If $y = ax^n$, then $\dfrac{dy}{dx} = nax^{n-1}$

Integration. $\displaystyle\int ax^n dx = \dfrac{ax^{n+1}}{n + 1} + \text{a constant}$

Turning Points. $\dfrac{dy}{dx}$ is zero

Maximum. As x increases, $\dfrac{dy}{dx}$ changes from $+$ to $-$.

Minimum. As x increases, $\dfrac{dy}{dx}$ changes from $-$ to $+$.

Area under curve: $\displaystyle\int_a^b y\,dx$

Volume of revolution: $\displaystyle\int_a^b \pi y^2 dx$

Velocity: $\dfrac{ds}{dt}$.   Acceleration: $\dfrac{dv}{dt}$

Polygon. Sum of interior angles: $(2n - 4)$ right angles
Sum of exterior angles: $360°$

$$\tan \theta = \frac{y}{x}, \quad \sin \theta = \frac{y}{z}, \quad \cos \theta = \frac{x}{z}$$

Pythagoras' Theorem: $x^2 + y^2 = z^2$
$$\sin^2 \theta + \cos^2 \theta = 1$$

If $\theta + \phi = 90°$, $\sin \phi = \cos \theta$

If θ is obtuse,

$\tan \theta = -\tan(180° - \theta)$, $\sin \theta = \sin(180° - \theta)$,
$\cos \theta = -\cos(180° - \theta)$

Sine Formula: $\dfrac{a}{\sin A} = \dfrac{b}{\sin B} = \dfrac{c}{\sin C} = 2R$,

where R is the circumradius of the triangle.

Cosine Formula: $a^2 = b^2 + c^2 - 2bc \cos A$

$$\cos A = \frac{b^2 + c^2 - a^2}{2bc}$$

Radius of Earth: 6.371×10^3 kilometres.

An international nautical mile is 1852 metres.

A knot is a speed of 1 nautical mile per hour.

MEASURES AND MONEY

EXERCISE I

1. Find the cost of 74 articles at 38p each.

2. Find the cost of 14.5 m at 32p per metre.

3. How many articles costing 62p each can be purchased for £21.70?

4. Find the cost of 1 m of cloth if 12.5 m cost 2250 francs.

5. Multiply £35.47 by 97.

6. Divide £1902.24 by 36.

7. Multiply 270 g by 84 and give the answer in kilogrammes.

8. Divide 14.4 m by 225. Answer in millimetres.

9. How many records costing 43p each can be purchased with a birthday gift of £5 and how much is left over?

10. Find the number of seconds in 3 h 47 min.

11. Find the cost of 3.4 tonnes at £15.60 per tonne.

12. Find the number of minutes between 10.45 a.m. and 2.10 p.m.

13. The rate of pay for a job is 45p per hour with time and a half for overtime. A normal working week is 40 hours. Find the wage for a man who works 48 hours.

14. A heating system uses 1240 litres of oil per day and is used for 175 days in the year. Calculate the cost of the oil for a year if 1000 litres costs £9.20.

15. A motorist averages 12 km to 1 litre of petrol. Calculate, correct to the nearest ten pence, his estimated cost of petrol for a journey of 940 km if 1 litre costs 7p.

16. A fence of length 42 m is built using posts costing 55p each and planks costing 6½p each. The posts are placed 3 m apart and 8 planks are used between each pair of posts. Find the total cost.

FRACTIONS

EXERCISE 2

Simplify:

1. $3\frac{5}{6} - 2\frac{3}{8} + 1\frac{2}{3}$

2. $4\frac{2}{3} - 1\frac{3}{4} - 2\frac{5}{12}$

3. $1\frac{7}{9} \times 1\frac{1}{4} \div \frac{2}{3}$

4. $1\frac{1}{4} \times 1\frac{2}{5} \div \frac{7}{8}$

5. $2\frac{2}{5} \div (2\frac{1}{4} - 1\frac{3}{4})$

6. $\frac{2}{3}$ of $(2\frac{1}{4} - 1\frac{1}{5})$

7. $(3\frac{3}{4} - 1\frac{2}{3}) \div 2\frac{2}{9}$

8. $(4\frac{1}{8} - 2\frac{5}{6} + 3\frac{1}{2}) \div 3\frac{5}{6}$

9. $\dfrac{3\frac{5}{6} - 2\frac{7}{12}}{3\frac{1}{2} - 1\frac{5}{8}}$

10. $\dfrac{4\frac{2}{5} + 1\frac{3}{3}}{3\frac{1}{3} - 2\frac{3}{4}}$

11. $\dfrac{\frac{1}{3} \times (4\frac{1}{2})^2}{\frac{5}{16} + \frac{1}{4}}$

12. $\dfrac{(3\frac{1}{2})^2}{2\frac{7}{10} + 3\frac{2}{15}}$

13. $\dfrac{2\frac{2}{5}}{2\frac{1}{4}} + \dfrac{4\frac{2}{3}}{3\frac{1}{2}}$

14. $\dfrac{1\frac{1}{5} + 4\frac{2}{3}}{2\frac{5}{6} + 4\frac{1}{2}}$

15. $(5\frac{2}{5} - 2\frac{4}{7}) \div (2\frac{8}{21} - 1\frac{4}{15})$ **16.** $4\frac{1}{12} - (1\frac{2}{3} \times 1\frac{5}{8})$

17. Multiply $\frac{2}{3} - (\frac{3}{8} + \frac{1}{6})$ by $(1\frac{2}{3} - \frac{3}{5})$.

18. Divide the sum of $1\frac{7}{12}$ and $4\frac{4}{15}$ by the sum of $\frac{3}{5}$ and $\frac{3}{8}$.

19. Find the squares of $3\frac{1}{2}$, $1\frac{2}{7}$ and $2\frac{3}{4}$ and the square roots of $1\frac{9}{16}$, $6\frac{1}{4}$ and $2\frac{14}{25}$.

20. Find the cubes of $1\frac{1}{2}$ and $2\frac{1}{3}$ and the cube roots of $2\frac{10}{27}$ and $5\frac{23}{64}$.

21. Find the difference between the greatest and the least of $\frac{2}{3}$, $\frac{3}{4}$ and $\frac{5}{7}$.

22. Find $\frac{1}{2}$ of $1\frac{1}{9}$, $\frac{1}{3}$ of $1\frac{5}{6}$ and $\frac{1}{4}$ of $2\frac{1}{3}$. Divide the greatest by the least.

23. Express 27 min as a fraction of a day.

24. Express $87\frac{1}{2}$p as a fraction of £2.

25. Express 375 m as a fraction of 4.5 km.

26. What fraction of £3.78 is 84p?

27. Express the area of a rectangular plot 125 m by 60 m as a fraction of a hectare.

5

DECIMALS

Evaluate, without tables:

1. 812.5×0.0224
2. 0.07625×7.36
3. $7.70739 \div 23.57$
4. $4.8928 \div 0.176$
5. $0.296893 \div 8.27$
6. $0.091008 \div 2.37$
7. $(0.94)^2 - (0.84)^2$
8. $(33.7)^2 - (16.3)^2$
9. $\dfrac{0.24 \times (0.03)^2}{0.072}$
10. $\dfrac{16.5}{2.1} \times \dfrac{0.14}{0.022}$
11. $\dfrac{0.115 \times 28.8}{8.28}$
12. $\dfrac{2.25 \times 15.4}{0.55 \times 350}$

Express as decimals:

13. $\frac{7}{16}$ and $\frac{19}{250}$
14. $\frac{3}{32}$ and $\frac{28}{625}$

15. Express as decimals, correct to 4 significant figures: $\frac{2}{3}$, $\frac{5}{11}$ and $\frac{3}{70}$.

16. Express as decimals, correct to 4 decimal places: $\frac{9}{13}$, $\frac{18}{19}$ and $\frac{17}{380}$.

17. Express 19 min 12 s as a decimal of 1 h.

18. Express 0.78 h in minutes and seconds.

19. Express 26½p as a decimal of £5.

20. Express 95p as a decimal of £1.25.

21. Divide 3.6659×10^2 by 7×10^{-3}.

22. Multiply 5.27×10^{-5} by 9×10^3.

Evaluate, correct to 3 significant figures:

23. $0.837 \div (19.09 - 6.42)$.

24. $3.142 \times 7.6^2 - 3.142 \times 4.4^2$.

AVERAGES AND SPEEDS

1. The average weekly wage of 8 men is 35 dollars; the wages of two other men are 37.5 dollars and 35.5 dollars. Find the average weekly wage of the ten men.

2. The average weight of eight parcels is 1.8 kg. When one parcel is removed the average weight of the others is 1.75 kg. Find the weight of the parcel removed.

3. In a concert hall there are 154 seats at 60p, 360 at 45p, 682 at 35p, 340 at 30p and 250 at 25p. Find, correct to the nearest penny, the average price of a seat.

4. What weight of a substance worth 15 fr per kg must be mixed with 24 kg worth 8 fr per kg to make a mixture worth 11 fr per kg?

5. A sprinter runs 100 m in 11 s. Find his average speed in km/h, correct to the nearest unit.

6. Express 54 km/h and 900 km/h in metres per second.

7. A man walking at 5 km/h takes 115 strides per minute. How many strides does he take in 100 m?

8. A car is travelling at 90 km/h. How many metres does it travel in 1 second?

9. A train is 160 m long. How many seconds does it take to pass an observer if its speed is 70 km/h?

10. A motorist travels 20 km in $\frac{1}{4}$ h, 60 km in 50 min and 17 km in 25 min. Find his average speed for the whole journey.

11. The average age of a class of 28 pupils is 16 yr 3 months. When eight pupils leave the average is reduced by 2 months. Calculate the average age of those who leave.

RATIO AND PROPORTION

Exercise 5

1. A sum of money is divided in the ratio 3 : 5. The larger part is £465. Find the smaller part.

2. A solution is made by dissolving 240 g of salt in 1.6 l of water. Calculate the ratio by mass of salt to water. [1 cm³ of water has a mass of 1 g.]

3. Three men are employed for 40 h, 45 h and 47 h respectively. Their total wage is £50.16. Calculate the hourly rate of pay and the wage of the man who works 45 h.

4. (i) Increase 60 in the ratio 5 : 4.
　　(ii) Decrease 80 in the ratio 4 : 5.

5. A sum of money is divided between A and B so that B gets a third as much again as A. If B receives £1.60, find the original sum.

6. At a base camp there is sufficient food to last 12 men for 50 days. After 15 days 7 men leave the camp. How much longer will the food last?

7. A model boiler contains 120 cm³. The scale is 1 : 25. Find the capacity of the actual boiler in litres.

8. If 9 looms weave 675 m of cloth in 5 h, how many metres will 4 looms weave in 6 h?

9. A contractor estimates that it will take 30 men working 8 hours a day 35 days to complete a job. He has only 24 men and wishes to do the job in 42 days. How many minutes overtime must the men work each day?

10. 5 litres of petrol have a mass of 3.4 kg. Find, in grammes, the mass of 1 cm³.

11. A fertilizer must be spread at the rate of 5 kg per are. How many kilogrammes are needed for a rectangular field 45 m × 25 m?

12. The scale of a map is 5 cm to 1 km. What distance in metres is represented by 24 mm and what area in hectares is represented by a rectangle 24 mm by 15 mm?

8

13. A bottle contains a litre of a solution. 250 cm³ is poured off and replaced by water. 100 cm³ of the weaker solution is then poured off and replaced by water. Find the ratio of water to the original solution.

14. A tourist changes travellers' cheques for £20 into Austrian currency at 61.20 schillings to £1. He spends 893 schillings and changes the remainder back into sterling at 61.60 schillings to £1. How much does he receive?

15. A man's income is £1530. ⅖ of it is free of tax, no tax is paid on the first £490 of the remainder, 30% is paid on the next £260 and 41.25% on the remainder. How much tax is paid?

16. In a certain city a rate of 1p in the £ produces £326 400. To cover the cost of education a rate of 9.7p in the £ is required. Calculate (i) the total cost of education and (ii) the share of this cost borne by a man whose house has a rateable value of £90.

17. A journey of 3990 km was made partly by air, partly by water and partly by land. The times spent in the air, on the water and on land were in the proportions 1 : 16 : 2 and the average speeds for these portions of the journey were in the proportions of 20 : 1 : 3. If the average speed for the whole journey was 42 km/h, find the times spent and the actual distances travelled by air, water and land respectively.

PERCENTAGES

Exercise 6

1. (i) Find 15% of £2.30.
   (ii) Express 12 fr 60 c as a percentage of 22 fr 50 c.
   (iii) Find the sum of money of which 38½p is 5½%.

2. Giving the answers correct to the nearest whole number:
   (i) Express 29 as a percentage of 85.
   (ii) Find 29% of 85.
   (iii) Find the number of which 85 is 29%.

3. After a reduction of 12%, the price of a chair is £5.50. Find the original price.

4. A house agent receives a commission of 5% of the first £300 of the price of a house and $2\frac{1}{2}$% of the remainder. Find his commission on a sale of £3250.

5. 450 oranges are bought for £7.20 and sold at 2p each. Find the gain per cent on the cost price.

6. A grocer buys 50 kg of tea for £25. At what price per 100 g must he sell it in order to gain 40% on the cost price?

7. By selling an article for £21.45 a man makes a profit of 32% on his cost price. Find his profit.

8. A discount of 10% is allowed on a bill. Find the original amount of a bill which is settled for £24.30.

9. (i) An article costing x francs is sold at a profit of y% of the cost price. Find the selling price.

    (ii) An article is sold for z francs. If the profit is y% of the cost price, find the cost price.

10. By selling an article for 7 dollars 50 cents a man makes 25% profit on the cost price. At what price should he sell it to make 30% profit on the cost price?

11. One tradesman calculates his percentage profit on the buying price and another calculates it on the selling price. Find the difference in actual profits if both tradesmen claim to make $17\frac{1}{2}$% profit on goods sold at £3760.

12. The retail cost of a £15 suit is made up of the following parts: wool 12%, cloth manufacture 16%, tailoring 44%, retailer's profit 28%. If the price of wool increases by $33\frac{1}{3}$% and the cost of cloth manufacture and tailoring by $16\frac{2}{3}$%, what will be the new price of the suit, allowing the retailer only the same *cash* profit?

What percentage increase in price is this?

13. Cloth is bought in England at £1.20 per metre and imported into France, where an import duty of 20% is paid. At what price per metre, to the nearest 0.01 franc, must the cloth be sold to give a profit of 40% on the outlay? [Take £1 = 13.32 fr.]

14. A and B join to form a business with capitals of £4200 and £6400 respectively. After 3 months they are joined by C with a capital of £5400. During the first 3 months the business makes a profit at the rate of 12% p.a. of the capital, and during the remaining 9 months of the first year the rate is 16% p.a. of the total capital. Find the amount received by each partner as his share of the profits for the first year.

15. The cost of manufacture of certain goods is divided between material and labour in the ratio 5 : 7. If the cost of material increases by 20% and the cost of labour decreases by 40%, find the resulting decrease per cent in the total cost of manufacture of the goods.

INTEREST

Exercise 7

In Questions 1 to 10 find the missing quantities, interest being calculated as simple interest.

	Principal	Rate %	Time yr	Interest	Amount
1.	£640	$3\frac{1}{2}$	5	?	?
2.	£125	4	?	£12.50	?
3.	£148.80	?	$2\frac{1}{2}$	£18.60	?
4.	£166.40	$4\frac{1}{2}$	$6\frac{1}{4}$	?	?
5.	£310	?	2	?	£353.40
6.	?	$5\frac{1}{2}$	$3\frac{3}{4}$	£75.90	?
7.	?	$7\frac{1}{2}$	8	?	£304
8.	£247	6	$3\frac{1}{2}$	?	?
9.	?	5	$1\frac{1}{3}$	?	£339.20
10.	?	$4\frac{1}{2}$	3	?	£1010.15

11. Find, correct to the nearest penny, the simple interest on £69.40 for 6 years 8 months at $3\frac{1}{2}$% p.a.

12. What sum of money, correct to the nearest pound, amounts to £200 in 4 years at $5\frac{1}{2}$% p.a. simple interest?

Find, to the nearest penny, the compound interest on:

13. £400 at 5% p.a. for 2 years.

14. £83.50 at 6% p.a. for 2 years.

15. £125 at 4% p.a. for 3 years.

16. £650 at $3\frac{1}{2}$% p.a. for 2 years.

17. Each year the value of a car falls by 10% of its value at the beginning of the year. Last 1st January the car was worth £450. What will it be worth next 1st January, and what was it worth on the previous 1st January?

18. A man invests £1500 in a building society paying $3\frac{3}{4}$% p.a. and £750 in the National Savings Bank paying $2\frac{1}{2}$% p.a. Express the interest he receives in a year as a percentage of his capital.

19. A man borrows £460 at 5% p.a. compound interest. At the end of each year he repays £100 in settlement of the interest for that year and to reduce the debt. Find how much he still owes after the fourth year.

20. During 1963 the population of a town decreased by 3.8% of its size at the beginning of the year. During 1964 and 1965 it increased by 2.1% and 3.2% respectively of its size at the beginning of the year. Calculate, correct to one decimal place, the percentage increase over the three-year period.

USE OF TABLES

EXERCISE 8

Find, correct to 4 significant figures:

1. $\sqrt{4.76}$, $\sqrt{47.6}$, $\sqrt{476}$, $\sqrt{0.00476}$, $\sqrt{0.0476}$

2. $\sqrt{93.47}$, $\sqrt{2624}$, $\sqrt{15.8}$, $\sqrt{15\ 800}$, $\sqrt{0.158}$

3. $\sqrt{0.432}$, $\sqrt{0.0432}$, $\sqrt{717.5}$, $\sqrt{0.7175}$, $\sqrt{57.69}$

4. $(67.3)^2$, $(562.3)^2$, $(0.763)^2$, $(0.0763)^2$, $(0.2384)^2$

5. $\dfrac{1}{8.54}$, $\dfrac{1}{85.4}$, $\dfrac{1}{0.3254}$, $\dfrac{1}{0.02363}$, $\dfrac{1}{423.4}$

6. $\sqrt{\frac{2}{7}}$, $\sqrt{\frac{2}{9}}$, $\sqrt{3\frac{1}{4}}$, $\sqrt{5\frac{7}{11}}$

Use logarithms to evaluate to 4 significant figures:

7. $7.294 \times 15.63 \times 3.729$

8. $9.683 \div 2.746$

9. $562.3 \div 41.92$

10. $\sqrt[3]{6725}$

11. $(2.793)^4$

12. $(84.38)^{\frac{3}{2}}$

13. $\dfrac{3.784 \times 29.07}{8.538}$

14. $\dfrac{460.7}{25.37 \times 8.605}$

15. 0.08329×7.647

16. $3.708 \div 0.579$

17. $0.932 \div 0.04709$

18. $(0.927)^3$

19. $\sqrt[3]{0.0465}$

20. $\sqrt[4]{0.02368}$

21. $(0.0848)^2$

22. $(0.00326)^{\frac{1}{2}}$

23. If $\log x = \frac{1}{3}(\bar{4}.9475)$, find x.

24. If $\log 2 = 0.30103$ find, without tables, $\log 4$, $\log 8$ and $\log 5$.

Use logarithms to evaluate to 3 significant figures:

25. $\left(\dfrac{0.829}{1.637}\right)^3$

26. $\sqrt[3]{\dfrac{7.205}{483.8}}$

27. $\dfrac{0.748 \times 5.292}{35.6}$

28. $\dfrac{0.7632}{0.279 \times 0.084}$

29. $\dfrac{32.74 \times \sqrt{96.82}}{0.504}$

30. $\dfrac{3.784 \times \sqrt{17.5}}{43.75}$

31. $\sqrt{(3.48)^2 + (5.73)^2}$

32. $\sqrt{(21.53)^2 - (10.04)^2}$

33. $\sqrt{0.8227 - (0.8227)^2}$

34. $(3.57)^3 + \sqrt[3]{2139}$

35. $73.8 \times \sqrt{\dfrac{0.0743}{0.8294}}$

36. $\dfrac{5.627 \times (0.234)^3}{\sqrt{0.8237}}$

37. $\dfrac{\sin 50°}{\sin 25°}$

38. $\dfrac{\sin 63° \, 20'}{\sin 80° \, 46'}$

39. $14.7 \ (\cos 65° \ 32')^2$

40. $(\tan 74° \ 50') \times (\sin 28° \ 16')$

41. $10^{2 \cdot 47} \div 10^{1 \cdot 98}$

42. $\sqrt[4]{\{10^{0 \cdot 78} \div 10^{3 \cdot 26}\}}$

43. $(0.0687)^{-3}$

44. $(0.5294)^{-\frac{2}{3}}$

MENSURATION: RECTILINEAR

EXERCISE 9

1. A rectangular field is 480 m long and 350 m wide. Calculate its perimeter in kilometres and its area in hectares.

2. A rectangular carpet has an area of 18.9 m². One side is 5.4 m. What is the other?

3. The floor of a room is 5.4 m by 4.4 m. Find the cost of staining a border of width 0.8 m round the outside of a carpet at $12\frac{1}{2}$p per m².

4. Find the area of $\triangle$ ABC if AB = AC = 15 cm and BC = 18 cm. Find also the width of a rectangle having the same area as $\triangle$ ABC and a length of 16 cm.

5. Find the area of a trapezium with parallel sides of 8 cm and 12 cm separated by 9 cm.

6. A metal pyramid has a square base of side 6 cm and a height of 8 cm. Find its volume.

It is melted down and cast into a prism having a square base of side 4 cm. Calculate the height of the prism.

7. Find the cost of painting the walls of a room 6.4 m long, 4 m wide and 3 m high, allowing window and door areas of 9 m², if one tin of paint covers 8 m² and costs 55p.

8. A rectangular tank is 2 m long, 1.4 m wide and 1.2 m high. Calculate its capacity in litres. What is the depth of water in the tank when it contains 2380 litres?

9. The external dimensions of a closed wooden box are 20 cm, 16 cm and 14 cm. If the wood is 1 cm thick, find the volume of the wood.

10. A tetrahedron has a base 6 cm $\times$ 8 cm $\times$ 10 cm and a vertical height of 12 cm. Calculate its volume.

11. A swimming bath is 50 m long and 20 m wide and its walls are vertical. The depths at the ends are 90 cm and 270 cm and the bottom slopes uniformly. Calculate, to the nearest tonne, the mass of water in the bath.

12. A rectangular tank 24 cm long and 15 cm wide contains water to a depth of 6 cm. A metal cube of side 10 cm is placed in the tank so that one face rests on the bottom. How many cubic centimetres of water must be poured into the tank so as to just cover the cube?

MENSURATION: CIRCULAR

Exercise 10

[Take π as $3\frac{1}{7}$.]

1. Find in metres the distance travelled by a bicycle wheel of diameter 63 cm when it makes 10 revolutions.

2. A wheel makes 25 revolutions when travelling 33 m. Find its diameter.

3. Find the area of a circle of radius 10.5 cm.

4. The area of a circle is 38.5 cm². Find its circumference.

5. The circumference of a circle is 55 cm. Find its area.

6. Find the volume of a cylindrical tin of height 11.2 cm and diameter 10 cm.

7. Find the curved surface area of a cylinder of height 8.4 cm and diameter 6.5 cm.

8. The curved surface area of a cylinder is 1584 cm². Find its height if its radius is 9 cm.

9. Find the volume and total surface area of a cylinder of radius 3.5 cm and height 6 cm.

10. Find the mass of a metal sphere of radius 3 cm if 1 cm³ of the metal has a mass of 10.5 g.

11. Find the radius and surface area of a sphere of volume $606\frac{2}{3}$ cm³.

12. A cone has a height of 2.8 cm and a base radius of 1.5 cm. Calculate its volume.

13. Calculate the total surface area of a cone of vertical height 12 cm and base radius 5 cm.

14. From a cone of height 12 cm and base radius 9 cm is cut a cone of height 8 cm. Calculate the volume of the remaining frustum.

15. A circular hole of diameter 7 cm is drilled in a rectangular metal plate 12 cm × 10 cm × $\frac{1}{2}$ cm. Calculate the volume of metal remaining.

16. A rectangle of length 21 cm and a circle of radius 10.5 cm have equal areas. Find the width of the rectangle.

17. How many cylindrical cups each of height 8 cm and diameter 7 cm can be filled from a cask containing 120 litres?

18. A storage tank consists of a cylinder with a hemisphere at each end. The total length is 270 cm and the radius is 60 cm. Calculate the capacity, correct to the nearest litre.

19. A lead pipe is 90 cm long and has a circular cross-section of internal diameter 43 mm and external diameter 48 mm. Calculate its mass in kilogrammes if 1 cm³ of lead has a mass of 11.4 g (3 sig. fig.).

20. Three lead spheres of radii 2 cm, 3 cm and 4 cm are melted down and cast into a single sphere. Find its radius (3 sig. fig.).

21. The diameter of a solid copper sphere is 2.74 cm. Find its mass if the mass of 1 cm³ of copper is 8.9 g.

If the sphere is placed in a cylinder having a diameter of 3.2 cm and containing water, by how much will the water level rise? (3 sig. fig.)

ALGEBRAIC SIMPLIFICATION

Simplify:

1. $3(a - 2b + c) - 2(a - b - 3c) + 5(b - c)$

2. $x(x + y - z) + y(y + z - x) + z(z + x - y)$

3. $5p(p - 2q) - 3q(2p + q) + 4(p^2 - q^2)$

4. $4(x^4 + x^2 - 1) - 3x(x^3 - 2x) - x^2(x^2 + 7)$

5. $4a^2b(a - 2b) + 3ab^2(2a - b) - ab(4a^2 - 3b^2)$

6. $(a + b)^2 + (a + b)(a - b) - 2ab$

7. $(e + 2f)(e - f) - (e - 3f)^2$

8. $(3 - g)(5 + 2g) + 2(3 - g)^2$

9. $3(x - 2) - \frac{2}{5}(x - 15)$

10. $(x - \frac{1}{3})^2 + \frac{4}{3}(x - \frac{1}{3})$

11. $3(2h + \frac{1}{h})(h + \frac{3}{h}) - (3h + \frac{1}{h})^2 - 2(\frac{2}{h} - h)^2$

12. $(4y + 1)(y^2 - 3y - 2)$

13. Multiply $p^2 + pq - q^2$ by $2p - 3q$.

14. Multiply $5 - 4x + 3x^2$ by $3 - 4x$.

15. Find the coefficient of x^3 and the constant term in the product of $(x^2 - 3x + 2)$ and $(3x^2 + 2x - 4)$.

16. Find the coefficient of y^2 and the coefficient of y in the product of $(3 - y + 2y^2)$ and $(5 + 2y - y^2)$.

17. Add $x + 5y$ and $x - 3y$. Subtract the result from $2x - 4y$.

18. What must be added to $(f - g)^2$ to give $(f + g)^2$?

19. Draw diagrams to illustrate:

(i) the identity $(x + 5)(x + 3) \equiv x^2 + 8x + 15$
and (ii) the expansion of $(3x + 2y)^2$.

20. If $x = a + b$ and $y = a - b$, express $x^2 + xy$ in terms of a and b.

21. If $c = x + 2y$ and $d = x - 2y$, express $c^2 - cd$ in terms of x and y.

22. If $a = 2x + y$ and $b = x - 2y$, express $(3a - b)(a + 3b)$ and $(2a + b)(a - 2b)$ in terms of x and y.

FACTORS

EXERCISE 12

Factorize:

1. $3a^2b + 6a^2c$ **2.** $15d^2 - 25de$ **3.** $\pi r^2 + 2\pi rh$

4. $a^2 - 4b^2$ **5.** $c^3 - 9c$ **6.** $25d^2 - 81e^2$

7. $18f^4 - 8$ **8.** $8g^3 - 50gh^2$ **9.** $m^4 - 16$

10. $3 - 3n^4$ **11.** $p^2 - 10p + 25$ **12.** $9r^2 + 12rt + 4t^2$

13. $12u^2 - 12u + 3$ **14.** $x^4 - 18x^2 + 81$

15. $(y - 3)^2 - 16z^2$ **16.** $(a + 3)^2 - a^2$

17. $4b^2 - (b - 2)^2$ **18.** $\pi a^2 - \pi b^2$

Find the value of a so that each of the following trinomials is a perfect square:

19. $x^2 - 14x + a$ **20.** $x^2 + 3x + a$ **21.** $4x^2 + 12x + a$

22. $25x^2 + 30xy + a$ **23.** $9x^4 - 15x^2 + a$

24. $16 - 12x + a$

25. Complete $x^2 + \frac{1}{3}x + \ldots = (\ldots)^2$.

26. Complete $x^2 - \frac{6}{5}x + \ldots = (\ldots)^2$.

Evaluate by factorizing:

27. $748^2 - 748 \times 728$ and $377 \times 296 - 292 \times 377$.

28. $303^2 - 297^2$ and $57^2 - 43^2$.

29. $(27\frac{1}{2})^2 - (17\frac{1}{2})^2$ and $(13.2)^2 - (6.8)^2$.

30. $\pi x^2 - \pi y^2$ if $\pi = \frac{22}{7}$, $x = 13$ and $y = 8$.

Factorize:

31. $ab - bc + ad - cd$ **32.** $fh + 5fj + 2gh + 10gj$

33. $m^2 + mp - 3mr - 3pr$ **34.** $xy - 4x - y^2 + 4y$

35. $ab - 3a + 5b - 15$ **36.** $3x - y - 6xy + 2y^2$
37. $cd^2 - c^2d - c + d$ **38.** $3 + 7f^2 - 6g - 14f^2g$
39. $6bt + 3ap - 9at - 2bp$ **40.** $a^2b^2 - 2abc + 5ab - 10c$
41. $x + y + x^2 - y^2$ **42.** $p^2 - 5p - q^2 + 5q$
43. $a^2b^2 - 9b^2 + 2a^2 - 18$ **44.** $1 - 2x - 4y^2 + 8xy^2$
45. $2fg - 10f + 4g - 20$ **46.** $12p - 3p^2 + 4pq - p^2q$
47. $x^2y^2 - x^2 - 4y^2 + 4$ **48.** $2 - 2a^2 + 4b^2 - 4a^2b^2$
49. $ax - ay + az + bx - by + bz$
50. $6 - 2c - 3d + cd + 3f - cf$

Factorize:

51. $a^2 + 5a + 6$ **52.** $b^2 - 9b + 8$ **53.** $c^2 + 2c - 8$
54. $d^2 - 7d - 18$ **55.** $1 + e - 2e^2$ **56.** $1 + 7f + 6f^2$
57. $10g^2 - 3g - 1$ **58.** $h^3 + 2h^2 - 3h$ **59.** $2j^2 - 2j - 12$
60. $3k - 24k^2 + 45k^3$ **61.** $l^4 - 20l^2 - 21$
62. $m^2 + 14mn + 24n^2$ **63.** $3a^2 + 5a + 2$
64. $5b^2 - 16b + 3$ **65.** $6c^2 + c - 15$
66. $2d^2 - d - 10$ **67.** $4e^2 + 5e - 6$ **68.** $28f^2 - 25f - 8$
69. $6g^2 + 23g + 21$ **70.** $5h^2 - 12hj + 4j^2$
71. $4k^2 - 9kl - 9l^2$ **72.** $10 - 11m - 6m^2$
73. $20n^2 - 35n - 75$ **74.** $54 + 3p^2 - 12p^4$
75. $2xy^2 - 5xy - 3x$ **76.** $7p^2q - 12pq^2 - 4q^3$
77. $(x - 4)^2 - 2(x - 4) - 15$
78. $20 - 12(y + 2) + (y + 2)^2$

79. Divide $10x^2 + 19x - 15$ by $5x - 3$.
80. Divide $3r^2 - 26rs + 16s^2$ by $3r - 2s$.
81. Find a if $x + 5$ is a factor of $x^2 + ax - 15$.
82. Find b if $x - 3$ is a factor of $x^2 + 4x + b$.
83. Find c if $2x + 3$ is a factor of $cx^2 - x - 15$.
84. Find d if $4 - 3x$ is a factor of $8 + dx - 9x^2$.
85. Factorize $4x^2 + 19x + 21$ and hence find the factors of 41 921.

86. Factorize $6x^2 + 11x + 3$ and hence find the factors of **713**.

87. Simplify $(4a - b)(a + 3b) + 2a(a - 2b)$ and factorize the result.

88. Simplify $(2x - y)^2 - 3y(x + y)$ and factorize the result.

SIMPLE EQUATIONS

EXERCISE 13

Solve:

1. $4(x - 2) - 3(2x - 1) + 5(8 - x) = 0$

2. $3(2y + 1) - 5(y - 2) = 2(3 - 2y)$

3. $2x(x + 3) - x(2x - 1) - 4 = 10$

4. $(x - 2)(x - 3) = (x + 4)(x + 1)$

5. $(y - 2)^2 - (y - 5)(y - 7) = 5$

6. $4(x - 1)^2 = 4x(x - 3) - 3(x + 5)$

7. $0.3x - 0.7 = 0.4x - 1.6$

8. $0.2(3x + 1) = 1.1x + 0.8$

9. $\frac{3}{4}x + \frac{1}{5}(4 - x) = 2$

10. $\frac{1}{2}y(y - 1) - \frac{1}{4}(2y^2 - 3) = 2y$

11. If $x = -2$ satisfies $3(ax + 7) = 4x - 1$, find a.

12. If $y = 3$ satisfies $(3b + y)^2 - (by + 4)^2 = 8$, find b.

13. If $4x - 9y = 3$, find y when $x = 2.1$.

14. If $(4p - 5)x - 4x + 9 = 0$ is satisfied by $x = -3$, find p.

15. Solve $5 + \sqrt{(4 + x)} = 8$.

16. Find three consecutive even numbers such that the sum of five times the smallest and seven times the middle number equals eleven times the largest number.

17. The angles of a triangle are $7(n + 1)$, $3(3n - 1)$ and $4(5n - 1)$ degrees. Find n and show that the triangle is isosceles.

18. A bag contains a certain number of 10p coins, three times as many 5p coins as 10p coins and seven more 2p than 5p coins. If the total value is £2, how many 10p coins are there?

19. A motorist does a journey of 178 km in $2\frac{3}{4}$ h. For the first $1\frac{1}{4}$ h his average speed is 16 km/h less than for the rest of the journey. Find his two average speeds.

20. The length and breadth of a rectangular flower bed are in the ratio 5 : 2. If the length is decreased by 1 m and the width is increased by 1 m, the area is increased by 0.8 m². Calculate the length.

21. A snack bar charges $2\frac{1}{2}$p per cup for tea and $3\frac{1}{2}$p per cup for coffee. For a total of 418 cups the amount received was £12.90. How many cups of tea were sold?

SIMULTANEOUS LINEAR EQUATIONS

Exercise 14

Solve the following equations for x and y:

1. $5x - 2y = 19$
$2x + y = 4$

2. $5x + 3y = 4$
$2x - y = 1$

3. $4x + 3y = 2$
$x + 4y = 7$

4. $x - 3y = 4$
$5x + 7y = 0$

5. $8x - 7y = 13$
$3x + 2y = 28$

6. $5x + 2y = 5$
$4x + 3y = -3$

7. $3x - y = 13$
$x - 3y = 15$

8. $4x - 5y = 3$
$2x - \frac{5}{6}y = 6\frac{1}{2}$

9. $3(x \times y) = 11$
$5x = 2 + 9y$

10. $4x - 7y = 3x - 5y + 1 = 2$

11. $0.5x + 0.2y = 1.2$ and $2x + 1.6y = 6$

12. $13x + y = x - 3y = 5$

13. $x + y = a$ and $x - y = b$

14. $ax - by = a^2 + b^2$ and $bx + ay = 2(a^2 + b^2)$

15. If $3x - 2y = 1\frac{1}{2}$ and $x + 3y = 11\frac{1}{2}$, find the value of $\dfrac{6x}{y}$.

16. $y = ax^2 + bx$ where a and b are constants. If $y = 6$ when $x = 2$ and $y = 21$ when $x = 3$, find a and b.

17. $px + qy = 7$ where p and q are constants. If $y = 1$ when $x = 5$ and $y = -1$ when $x = 2$, find y when $x = -4$.

18. Two numbers are such that if 21 is added to the first the answer is twice the second and if 9 is added to the second the answer is twice the first. Find the numbers.

19. A packet contains x five pence coins and y two pence coins, the total value being £4.30. If it had contained y five pence coins and x two pence coins the value would have been £3.40. Find x and y.

20. 5 ten pence coins and 7 fifty pence coins together have a mass of 151 g; 15 ten pence coins and 11 fifty pence coins together have a mass of 318 g. Find the mass of a ten pence coin and the mass of a fifty pence coin.

21. 15 litres of petrol and 2 litres of oil cost £1.48; 10 litres of petrol and 3 litres of oil cost £1.37. Find the cost of 1 litre of oil.

22. If 2 is added to both the numerator and denominator of a certain fraction, its value becomes $\frac{3}{4}$. If 3 is subtracted from both the numerator and denominator, its value becomes $\frac{2}{3}$. Find the fraction.

QUADRATIC EQUATIONS

EXERCISE 15

Solve the equations:

1. $x^2 - 7x + 12 = 0$

2. $x^2 - 3x - 10 = 0$

3. $2x^2 + 5x - 3 = 0$

4. $2x^2 + 5x = 0$

5. $x(6x + 1) = 12$

6. $18x^2 - 21x + 5 = 0$

7. $9x^2 - 24x + 16 = 0$

8. $\frac{2}{9}x^2 - 8 = 0$

9. $(3x - 4)^2 = 12\frac{1}{4}$

10. $4x(x - 1) - 15 = 0$

11. $3 - 11x = 4x^2$

12. $0.9x^2 + 6.3x = 0$

13. $(2x + 3)(x + 2) = 55$ **14.** $(1 - 2x)^2 = x^2$

15. $(7x - 8)(x + 1) + 2x^2 = 0$ **16.** $3(2x - 1)^2 = 18 - x$

Find equations with the following roots:

17. $5, -3$ **18.** $\frac{1}{3}, \frac{3}{4}$ **19.** $-2\frac{1}{2}, 1\frac{1}{5}$ **20.** $-3\frac{1}{2}, 0$

21. One root of $3x^2 + bx - 12 = 0$ is $1\frac{1}{3}$. Find b and the other root.

22. One root of $4x^2 - 17x + c = 0$ is 5. Find c and the other root.

Solve the equations, giving your answers correct to 2 decimal places:

23. $x^2 - 6x - 11 = 0$ **24.** $x^2 + 7x - 10 = 0$

25. $2x^2 + 5x - 9 = 0$ **26.** $3x^2 + 11x + 5 = 0$

27. $3x^2 - 6x + 1 = 0$ **28.** $5x^2 - 6x - 7 = 0$

29. $x + \dfrac{3}{x} = 14$ **30.** $x(2x - 3) = 4$

31. $2x(x - 4) = 5$ **32.** $5x^2 + 10x + 3 = 0$

33. The sides of a rectangle are $3x$ cm and $(x + 3)$ cm, and the diagonal is $(4x - 3)$ cm. Find x and the area of the rectangle.

34. A certain set of three integers can be used as the sides of a right-angled triangle. The largest exceeds the smallest by 50 and exceeds the other by 9. Find the integers.

35. Four numbers satisfy $x^2 + y^2 + z^2 = t^2$. If $y = x + 4$, $z = y + 5$ and $t = z + 4$, find x.

36. When four square metal plates are arranged in order of size, the lengths of consecutive plates differ by one centimetre. The total area of the four plates is 86 cm². Find the area of the smallest.

37. Two years ago a man's age was 3 times the square of his daughter's age. In three years' time his age will be 4 times her age. Find her present age.

38. A rectangular plate is 40 cm long and 30 cm wide. A rectangle is cut out, leaving an L-shaped plate. Both limbs of the L are the same width and the area is half that of the original plate. Find the width of each limb of the L.

FRACTIONS

Simplify:

1. $\dfrac{6ab}{2bc}$; $\quad \dfrac{-d^2}{de}$; $\quad \dfrac{7f^7}{3f^3}$; $\quad \dfrac{-12g^2}{9gh}$

2. $\dfrac{15km}{25m^2}$; $\quad \dfrac{3n^3}{-6np}$; $\quad \dfrac{-9s}{-3s^2}$; $\quad \dfrac{8t^5v^2}{-4tv}$

3. $\dfrac{x+y}{y+x}$; $\quad \dfrac{x-y}{y-x}$; $\quad \dfrac{x-y}{x+y}$; $\quad \dfrac{-x-y}{x+y}$

4. $\dfrac{2a-2b}{6a-6b}$

5. $\dfrac{c^2-d^2}{c+d}$

6. $\dfrac{f^2g-fg^2}{f^2g^2}$

7. $\dfrac{5h-15}{h^2-2h-3}$

8. $\dfrac{k^2+4k+3}{k^2+3k}$

9. $\dfrac{18m^2-50}{9m^2+30m+25}$

10. $\dfrac{3n^2-12p^2}{6n^2+12np}$

11. $\dfrac{r^2tv-rt^2x}{ryv-ytx}$

12. $\dfrac{9-\dfrac{1}{x^2}}{3x+1}$

Complete:

13. $\dfrac{3a}{b}=\dfrac{3a^2}{b^2}=\dfrac{3a^2}{}=\dfrac{}{-3b}=\dfrac{}{b(b+1)}$

14. $\dfrac{5}{cd}=\dfrac{5d}{}=\dfrac{}{-2cd}=\dfrac{5(d-c)}{}=\dfrac{}{c^2d-cd^2}$

15. $\dfrac{2}{f-3}=\dfrac{}{3-f}=\dfrac{6f}{}=\dfrac{}{f^2-9}=\dfrac{}{(f-3)^2}$

Simplify:

16. $\dfrac{5a}{6}+\dfrac{2a}{3}-\dfrac{a}{4}$

17. $\dfrac{3}{4b}-\dfrac{7}{10b}+\dfrac{2}{5b}$

18. $\dfrac{3}{c}+\dfrac{2}{d}-\dfrac{5}{e}$

19. $\dfrac{1}{3fg}-\dfrac{5}{6gh}-\dfrac{1}{2fh}$

20. $\dfrac{k+3}{6} - \dfrac{k-2}{4} + \dfrac{3k+1}{3}$ **21.** $\dfrac{m-3}{2m} - \dfrac{p-2}{3p}$

22. $\dfrac{x+2}{x} - \dfrac{x+4}{x+2}$ **23.** $\dfrac{5}{y+3} + \dfrac{3}{y-5}$

24. $\dfrac{4}{3a-2b} - \dfrac{2}{2a-b}$ **25.** $\dfrac{3c}{c-2} + \dfrac{5c}{3c-6}$

26. $\dfrac{5d^2+10d}{d+2} - \dfrac{20-10d}{2-d}$ **27.** $\dfrac{3}{1+3f} - \dfrac{1}{1+f}$

28. $\dfrac{g+h}{g-h} - \dfrac{g-h}{g+h}$ **29.** $\dfrac{1}{k-m} - \dfrac{k-3m}{(k-m)(k+3m)}$

30. $\dfrac{4}{n^2-2n-3} - \dfrac{3}{n^2-3n}$ **31.** $\dfrac{5p}{p^2-9} + \dfrac{2}{p+3}$

32. $\dfrac{3}{q+v} - \dfrac{3q+v}{q^2+qv}$ **33.** $\dfrac{1}{x^2+3x+2} - \dfrac{1}{x^2+5x+6}$

34. $\dfrac{5a^3}{2b^2} \div \dfrac{15ac}{6b}$ **35.** $\dfrac{d(f+d)}{3d^2} \times \dfrac{6d^3}{f+d}$

36. $\dfrac{a+2}{a^2-9} \times \dfrac{a^2-5a+6}{a-2}$ **37.** $\dfrac{b^2-4}{4b} \times \dfrac{6b^2}{(b+2)^2}$

38. $\left(\dfrac{7}{c} - \dfrac{3}{d}\right) \div \dfrac{4}{d}$

39. Find the square root of $\left(\dfrac{x}{y}\right)^2 + \left(\dfrac{y}{x}\right)^2 + 2$.

40. Find the square root of $\dfrac{p^2}{9} + \dfrac{1}{p^2} - \dfrac{2}{3}$.

EQUATIONS INVOLVING FRACTIONS

EXERCISE 17

Solve the equations:

1. $\dfrac{x}{3} + \dfrac{x}{5} = 4$ **2.** $\dfrac{x}{2} - \dfrac{x+3}{4} = 1$

3. $\dfrac{3x}{4} + \dfrac{4-x}{5} = 2$ **4.** $\dfrac{4x+1}{5} - \dfrac{4x-11}{3} = \dfrac{2x+5}{6}$

5. $(x-1) - \frac{1}{2}(x-2) = \frac{1}{3}(x-3)$

6. $\frac{2}{5}(3x-8) - \frac{1}{7}(4x-3) = 1$

7. $\dfrac{1}{3x} + \dfrac{1}{4x} = 3\frac{1}{2}$ **8.** $x = \dfrac{3}{x} + \dfrac{1}{2}$

9. $\dfrac{x+3}{x} = \dfrac{x}{x-5}$ **10.** $\dfrac{4}{3x-2} = \dfrac{1}{2x-1}$

11. $\dfrac{12}{x} - \dfrac{9}{x+3} = 1$ **12.** $\dfrac{5}{x-2} + \dfrac{3}{x} = \dfrac{1}{2x}$

13. $\dfrac{x-1}{x+5} = \dfrac{1}{x-1}$ **14.** $\dfrac{x}{1-x^2} = \dfrac{5}{24}$

15. $\dfrac{1}{3x-2} + \dfrac{2}{x} = \dfrac{3}{x+1}$ **16.** $\dfrac{3}{3x+2} + \dfrac{2}{3x-2} = \dfrac{3}{9x^2-4}$

17. A hiker finds that he has 31 min in which to catch the last train from a station 4 km away. If he can walk at 6 km/h and run at 15 km/h, how far must he run in order to catch the train?

18. 216 sweets are to be distributed between a certain number of children. As three of the children are absent the others each get one extra sweet. Find the number of children present.

19. A club has £255 with which to purchase some chairs. It is offered a discount of 25p per chair and can then purchase 16 more chairs than expected. Find the full cost of a chair.

20. A motorist makes a journey of 225 km. He returns by a different route of 240 km at an average speed which is 10 km/h greater than on the outward journey and takes 30 min less. Find the two average speeds.

21. Last year the members of a club paid £42 in subscriptions. This year the membership has increased by 20 and the subscription has been reduced by 10p per member. The club income is now £45. How many members has the club?

FORMULAE: CONSTRUCTION

1. A secretary buys x stamps at k pence each and y stamps at m pence each. How much change does she receive from a £1 note?

2. The dimensions of a rectangular block are x m, y m and z m. Find the surface area in square metres.

3. A car is travelling at x km/h. How many metres does it travel in t minutes?

4. A train is travelling at y km/h. How many seconds does it take to travel l metres?

5. A boat travels n km upstream at x km/h and returns downstream to its starting point at y km/h. Find the total time taken.

6. A man is paid x pence per hour for a normal week of y hours and double this rate for overtime. Find his wage in pounds for a week of n hours. ($n > y$.)

7. Two prize winners share £1 in the ratio $x : y$. State, in pence, the sum received by each.

8. Find the total selling price of x articles which cost y pence each and are sold at a profit of z per cent of the cost price.

9. Express algebraically: 'Four times the product of two numbers is equal to the square of their difference subtracted from the square of their sum.'

10. A rectangular swimming pool, p m long and q m wide, is surrounded by a concrete border of width w m. Find the area of the border.

11. The scale of a map is x m to 1 cm. Find the area in ares of a field represented on the map by a rectangle p cm by q cm.

12. A car does k kilometres to a litre of petrol which costs p pence. Find the cost in pounds for a journey of x kilometres.

13. A batsman has an average of m runs per innings for x innings one season and n runs per innings for y innings the next season. Find his average for the two seasons taken together.

14. I run for t_1 min at x_1 km/h and walk for t_2 min at x_2 km/h. Find my average speed for the whole distance.

15. A man drives m_1 km at v_1 km/h and m_2 km at v_2 km/h. Find the average speed for the journey.

16. Write down five consecutive odd numbers taking the middle one as x. Show that the average of the squares of the five numbers exceeds the square of the middle one by 8.

17. The value £z of a car costing originally £x falls by £y in the first year, by £$\frac{3}{4}y$ in the second year and by £$\frac{3}{8}y$ in each of the following years.

   (i) Find the formula for z after n years where $n > 2$.

   (ii) If a car costing £740 is worth £372 after 5 years, find y.

18. Find the angle in degrees between the two hands of a clock at m minutes past h o'clock. (Assume $m > h$.)

Use the result to find the time between 2 o'clock and 3 o'clock at which the hands are in a straight line.

FORMULAE: EVALUATION

Exercise 19

Find the value of:

1. $a^2b^3 - a^3b^2$ when $a = -4$ and $b = -1\frac{1}{2}$.

2. $(4c - d)/(c^2 - d^2)$ when $c = -2$ and $d = 1$.

3. $(f - 3g)^2 - f^2 - 3g^2$ when $f = 5$ and $g = -3$.

4. $\dfrac{(a - b)(c - d)}{ac - bd}$ when $a = 3$, $b = 1$, $c = 2$ and $d = -\frac{1}{2}$.

5. $\dfrac{p + q}{p + t}$ when $p = 3.67$, $q = 0.83$ and $t = 2.33$.

6. $2\pi\sqrt{\dfrac{l}{g}}$ when $\pi = 3\frac{1}{7}$, $l = 98$ and $g = 32$.

7. $\dfrac{5a + 7b}{10a + 3b}$ when $a = 3t$ and $b = 5t$.

8. If $x : y = 3 : 2$, calculate the value of $(4x + y) : (5y - 2x)$.

9. If $7x - 5y = \frac{1}{6}(3y - 2x)$, find the value of $\dfrac{(8x + 3y)}{(8x - 3y)}$.

10. From $\dfrac{1}{f} = (\mu - 1)\left(\dfrac{1}{r} - \dfrac{1}{R}\right)$, find the value of f when $\mu = 1.6$, $r = 6\frac{2}{3}$ and $R = 7\frac{1}{2}$.

Use tables to find the value of:

11. $\dfrac{w}{610.4}\sqrt{\dfrac{m}{r}}$ when $r = 7.821$, $m = 1530$ and $w = 705.6$.

12. $\dfrac{a^3 + b^3}{a + b}$ when $a = 0.7152$ and $b = 0.2169$.

FORMULAE: MANIPULATION

EXERCISE 20

Change each formula to make the given letter the subject:

1. $c = 2\pi r$; r

2. $A = \pi r^2$; r

3. $\dfrac{y}{x} = \tan A$; y

4. $\dfrac{x}{h} = \cos A$; h

5. $n = \sqrt{\dfrac{a}{b}}$; b

6. $y = \dfrac{1}{x} + c$; x

7. $v = u + at$; t

8. $v^2 = u^2 + 2fs$; u

9. $T = \dfrac{\lambda(x - a)}{a}$; x

10. $x = \dfrac{3 - 8y}{2 + 3y}$; y

11. $p = \dfrac{ra - b}{r - a}; r$

12. $a^2 x^2 + b = c; x$

13. $n = \dfrac{p}{\sqrt{(h^2 + k^2)}}; h$

14. $T = \sqrt{\dfrac{PQ}{R + S}}; S$

15. $\cos \theta = \dfrac{1 - t^2}{1 + t^2}; t$

16. $\dfrac{p}{x} = \dfrac{q}{t} + \dfrac{q}{x}; x$

✓ **17.** $s = ut + \tfrac{1}{2} ft^2; f.$ If $t = 6$, $u = 1\tfrac{1}{2}$, $s = 36$, find f.

✓ **18.** $a = b + \sqrt{b^2 + c^2}; c.$ If $a = 8$, $b = 3$, find c.

✓ **19.** $A = P\left(1 + \dfrac{RT}{100}\right); T.$ If $A = 392$, $P = 350$, $R = 4$, find T.

✓ **20.** $S = 2\pi r(r + h); h.$ If $S = 165$, $r = 3\tfrac{1}{2}$, $\pi = 3\tfrac{1}{7}$, find h.

✓ **21.** $\dfrac{1}{v} - \dfrac{1}{u} = \dfrac{1}{f}; v.$ If $f = 20$, $u = 16$, find v.

22. If $a = 2b + 3$ and $b = 1 + \dfrac{2}{c}$, express $\dfrac{a + 3}{a - 1}$ in terms of c.

23. If $\dfrac{9a + 2b}{a + b} = 7$, express a in terms of b and find the value of $\dfrac{2a + 9b}{a + b}$.

24. If $x = \dfrac{p + r}{p - r}$ and $y = \dfrac{x - 1}{x + 1}$, express y in terms of p and r.

25. The length of a rectangle is k times its breadth and its perimeter is p cm. Find its area in terms of k and p.

26. The number x is increased by $r\%$ of itself and the number y is decreased by $r\%$ of itself. If the results are equal, express r in terms of x and y.

INDICES

Evaluate:

1. $8^{\frac{1}{3}}$, 3^{-2}, 5^0, $9^{\frac{3}{2}}$, $(\frac{16}{25})^{\frac{1}{2}}$

2. $27^{\frac{2}{3}}$, $16^{-\frac{1}{2}}$, $(\frac{2}{5})^{-2}$, $(\frac{1}{81})^{\frac{1}{4}}$, $8^{-\frac{4}{3}}$

3. $16^{\frac{3}{4}}$, 5^{-1}, $(\frac{9}{16})^{-\frac{1}{2}}$, 32^0, $(0.25)^{-\frac{3}{2}}$

4. $49^{-\frac{1}{2}}$, $\dfrac{1}{5^{-2}}$, $\dfrac{1}{(0.5)^3}$, $(36\frac{1}{3})^{\frac{3}{2}}$, $(6\frac{1}{4})^{-\frac{1}{2}}$

5. $8^{\frac{2}{3}} + 8^0 - 2^{-2}$

6. $81^{\frac{3}{4}} - (\frac{1}{5})^{-1} - 27^0$

7. $(\frac{1}{27})^{-\frac{1}{3}} + (\frac{1}{3})^{-2} + 16^{\frac{1}{2}}$

8. $4^{\frac{1}{2}} \times 3^{-2} \div 8^{-\frac{2}{3}}$

9. $(x-1)^{\frac{4}{3}} + (x+7)^{\frac{3}{4}} + (3x)^0$ when $x = 9$

10. Express as a single power of 2: $8^{\frac{5}{3}} \times 64^{\frac{1}{2}} \times 4^{-3}$.

11. Express as a single power of 3: $9^{-2} \times 81^{\frac{3}{2}} \times 27^{\frac{2}{3}}$.

12. Find p and w if $2^p = 128$ and $10^w = 0.001$.

13. Find x and y if $27^x = 81$ and $8^y = \frac{1}{4}$.

14. If $\sqrt[3]{(a^5b^{-4})} = a^x b^y$, find x and y.

Simplify:

15. $a^5 \times a^{-2}$, $b^7 \div b^{-5}$, $(c^{\frac{1}{3}})^{\frac{1}{3}}$, $(d^6)^{-\frac{1}{2}}$

16. $e^5 \times e^6 \times e^{-8}$, $f^{\frac{1}{2}} \times f^{\frac{1}{3}}$, $\left(\dfrac{g}{h}\right)^{-1}$, $\dfrac{1}{k^{-3}}$

17. $2^{\frac{1}{2}} \times 2 \times 3^{-2}$, $a^{-2} \times b^5 \times a^7$, $3p^{-1} \div 6p^2$, $6q^6 \div 2q^{-2}$

18. $x^{\frac{1}{3}}(x^{\frac{1}{3}} + 5 - 2x^{-\frac{1}{3}})$

19. $(y^{\frac{3}{4}}z^{-\frac{1}{2}})^{\frac{4}{3}}$ and $(4x^{-4})^{-\frac{1}{2}}$

20. $(x^{\frac{1}{2}} - x^{-\frac{1}{2}})^2$ and $(x^{\frac{2}{3}} + x^{-\frac{2}{3}})(x^{\frac{2}{3}} - x^{-\frac{2}{3}})$

GRAPHS FROM STATISTICAL DATA

1. A cyclist starts from his home at 11 a.m. and cycles to Scarborough, which is 80 km away. He cycles until 12.15 p.m. at 20 km/h and then stops for lunch. At 1 p.m. he starts again and cycles at 15 km/h until 4 p.m. After resting for $\frac{3}{4}$ h he finishes the journey at 20 km/h. Draw a graph of his journey, taking 2 cm to represent 1 h and to represent 10 km. From the graph find the time of his arrival.

His parents leave home at 1.30 p.m. and travel to Scarborough by car at an average speed of 60 km/h. When and where do they pass him?

2. At 1 p.m. a pipe commenced to feed an empty 3000-litre tank at the rate of 600 litres per hour. Some time later the rate of flow was reduced to 360 litres per hour and at 7.30 p.m. the tank was full. Find graphically the time at which the change occurred. [Take 2 cm to represent 1 hour and 400 litres.]

3. A hiker leaves village A at 10.10 a.m. to walk to village C, 24 km from A, passing through village B on the way. B is 7 km from A. After walking a certain distance he is picked up by a lorry and taken the rest of the journey at an average speed of 30 km/h. He noted that he passed through B at 11.28 and reached C at 12.10. Find graphically the time he was picked up and his walking speed. [Take 1 cm to 2 km and 1 cm to 10 min.]

Find also the latest time at which he could have got a lift by a car travelling at 60 km/h so as to reach C by 12.10.

4. Water is poured into a vessel at a steady rate and the height, h centimetres, after t seconds is given by the following table:

t	0	0.5	1.0	1.5	2.0	2.5	3.0	3.5	4.0	4.5	5.0	5.5	6.0
h	0	0.1	0.3	0.6	1.0	1.7	3.0	4.3	5.0	5.4	5.7	5.9	6.0

Plot a graph of h against t, taking 2 cm as the unit on both axes.

State the height after 1.7 sec and after 4.3 sec.

Describe the shape of the vessel.

Water is poured uniformly into a second vessel which is cylindrical. At 2, 4, 6 sec the heights are 2.8, 3.4, 4.0 cm respectively. Plot a graph for this vessel using the same axes.

What was the level of the water initially?

State the equation of the graph in the form $h = at + b$.

5. The table shows the amount £A owed after x years by a man who borrowed £4000 and repaid a fixed sum each year.

x	0	2	4	6	8	10	12
A	4000	3590	3138	2640	2088	1482	814

Draw a graph showing x and A and estimate the amount owing (i) after 5 yr, (ii) after 11 yr.

At the time he borrowed £4000 he also invested £1500 at 4% p.a. simple interest. Draw a graph to show the growth of this investment. When does this sum exceed his debt?

VARIATION

EXERCISE 23

1. Express (a) with a 'variation' sign
and (b) with an 'equals' sign and a constant:
  (i) y varies directly as x^2.
  (ii) S varies inversely as t.
  (iii) T varies directly as the square root of l.
  (iv) h is inversely proportional to the cube of r.

2. Complete the following:
  (i) If $y \propto x^2$, then $x \propto$.
  (ii) If $t \propto \dfrac{1}{v}$, then $v \propto$.
  (iii) If $r \propto \sqrt{A}$, then A $\propto$.

3. Sketch a graph to illustrate each of the following types of variation:

(i) $y \propto x$, (ii) $y \propto x^2$, (iii) $y \propto \dfrac{1}{x}$.

4. If $y = 4$ when $x = 3$, write down, without simplifying, the value of y when $x = 5$:

(i) if $y \propto x$; (ii) if $y \propto x^2$; (iii) if $y \propto \dfrac{1}{x}$; (iv) if $y \propto \dfrac{1}{\sqrt{x}}$.

5. If $y \propto x^2$ and $y = 9$ when $x = 4$, find y when $x = 1$ and find x when $y = 4$.

6. If $y \propto \dfrac{1}{x}$ and $y = 8$ when $x = 3$, find y when $x = 4$ and find x when $y = 12$.

7. When $x = 2$, $y = 8$. Find y when $x = 3$

(i) if y varies directly as the square of x;

(ii) if y varies inversely as the square of x.

8. y is inversely proportional to x^2 and when $x = 12$, $y = 1\frac{1}{2}$. Find y when $x = 9$ and find x when $y = 150$.

For what value of x is $y = x$?

9. z varies directly as the sum of x and y. When $x = 2$ and $y = 6$, $z = 24$. Find x such that $z = 27$ when $y = 5$.

10. $z \propto \dfrac{x^2}{y}$. If x is increased by 20% and y is decreased by 20%, find the percentage change in z.

11. If $w \propto r^2h$ and $w = 5$ when $r = 3$ and $h = 2$, find w when $r = 2$ and $h = 3$ and express w in terms of r and h.

12. A stone dropped from the top of a cliff of height h metres takes t seconds to reach the sea, where t varies as the square root of h. If $t = 3$ when $h = 43.2$, find t when $h = 58.8$ and find h when $t = 5$.

13. The volume of a given mass of gas is inversely proportional to its pressure. When the pressure is 80 cm of mercury, the volume is 300 cm^3. Find (i) the pressure when the volume is 400 cm^3, (ii) the volume when the pressure is 50 cm of mercury, and (iii) a formula between p and v.

14. y is the sum of two quantities A and B. A varies inversely as x and B varies directly as x. When $x = 4$, $y = 17$ and when $x = 6$, $y = 13$. Find y when $x = 10$ and find x when $y = 11\frac{1}{2}$.

15. The weekly cost £C of running an hotel consists of the sum of two parts, the first of which is constant and the second is proportional to the number of guests x. In one week there were 40 guests and the cost was £405; in another week there were 50 guests and the cost was £480. Find the formula for C in terms of x and the cost when there are 36 guests.

GRAPHS OF FUNCTIONS

EXERCISE 24

Sketch the graphs of:

1. $y = x$, $y = x^2$, $y = 5 - x^2$ and $xy = 12$.

2. $y = 3x + 5$, $y = -2x + 3$, $y = \frac{1}{2}x - 4$,
$3x + 4y + 8 = 0$ and $5x - 2y - 6 = 0$.

3. State the gradients of lines perpendicular to lines having gradients of 2, -5, $\frac{2}{3}$, $-\frac{1}{4}$, $-1\frac{3}{5}$.

4. The straight line $y = \frac{3}{4}x + 9$ meets the y axis at A and the x axis at B. Find the equations of the lines through A and B perpendicular to the given line.

5. Draw the graph of the function $4 + 2x - x^2$ for values of x from -2 to $+4$.

State (i) the maximum value of the function; (ii) the range of values of x for which the function is greater than 3.

Use the graph to find approximate solutions of the equations
(i) $4 + 2x - x^2 = 0$, (ii) $x^2 - 2x - 6 = 0$.

6. Draw the graphs of $y = \frac{1}{2}x^2 - 3x + 5$ and $y = 2 - \frac{1}{4}x$ for values of x from 0 to 6.

Find (i) the least value of y on the first graph; (ii) the range of values of x for which $2 - \frac{1}{4}x > \frac{1}{2}x^2 - 3x + 5$; (iii) the values of x for which $2 - \frac{1}{4}x$ exceeds $\frac{1}{2}x^2 - 3x + 5$ by 0.5.

7. Draw the graph of $y = \frac{1}{4}x^3$ from $x = 0$ to $x = 6$. Use the graph to find approximate values of $\sqrt[3]{100}$ and $\sqrt[3]{200}$.

Draw the graph of $y = 30 - 5x$ and find the value of x at its point of intersection with $y = \frac{1}{4}x^3$. What equation has this value of x as one root?

8. Draw the graph of $y = 4 - \dfrac{3}{x}$ from $x = \frac{1}{2}$ to $x = 5$.

Draw the tangent to the curve at $x = 2$ and by reading off its gradient find its equation.

Draw also the straight line $y = x - 1$. State, in its simplest form, the equation whose roots are given by the points of intersection of the two graphs and state the approximate values of these roots.

9. A rectangle is to have a perimeter of 120 cm. If the area is A cm^2 when the length of one side is x cm, express A in terms of x.

Draw the graph of $y = (60 - x)x$ from $x = 0$ to $x = 60$, taking 1 cm on the x axis to represent 5 cm and 1 cm on the y axis to represent 50 cm.

State the maximum area and find the dimensions of the rectangle which has an area of 800 cm^2.

10. Draw the graph of $y = x^2(4 - x)$ from $x = -1$ to $x = 4$, plotting points at $\frac{1}{2}$-unit intervals.

State (i) the maximum value of y; (ii) the minimum value of y; (iii) the roots of $x^3 - 4x^2 + 4 = 0$.

Draw the tangent at (1, 3) and state its gradient.

Draw the graph of $2y = x + 6$ and state the values of x at its points of intersection with the graph of $y = x^2(4 - x)$. What equation has these values as roots?

What graph would enable you to find the roots of $2x^3 - 8x^2 - x + 8 = 0$?

11. Draw the graph of $y = 2^x$ from $x = -2$ to $x = +2$, given that when $x = -\frac{3}{2}, -\frac{1}{2}, \frac{1}{2}, \frac{3}{2}, y = 0.35, 0.71, 1.41, 2.83$.

For what value of x is $2^x = 3$?

Draw the graph of $y = 2 - \frac{1}{2}x$.

State the range of values of x for which $2^x < 2 - \frac{1}{2}x$.

Find the value of x for which $2^x + \frac{1}{2}x = 3$.

12. Draw the graph of $y = \dfrac{4x + 1}{x + 5}$ from $x = -3$ to $x = +3$.

Draw also the graph of $x + 2y + 7 = 0$.

State the co-ordinates of the point of intersection of the graphs. What equation, in its simplest form, has the value of x at this point as a root?

13. Draw the graphs of $y = \log_{10}x$ and $y = \dfrac{3}{x + 4}$ from $x = 1$ to $x = 6$.

Hence find a root of $(x + 4)\log_{10}x = 3$.

Draw a third graph from which you can find a root of $(x + 4)\log_{10}x = 6$ and state this root.

DIFFERENTIATION

EXERCISE 25

Differentiate:

1. $x^3, \quad 5x^2, \quad 7x, \quad \dfrac{5}{x}, \quad \dfrac{6}{x^2} \quad$ and $\quad x + 8$

2. $4x^3 - 2x + 5$ **3.** $3x^2 + 4 - \dfrac{5}{x^2}$ **4.** $\dfrac{x^3 + x^2}{x}$

5. $(3 - x)^2$ **6.** $5t - 2t^2 - t^3$

Find $\dfrac{dy}{dx}$ if:

7. $y = 5 - \frac{1}{2}x + \frac{1}{3}x^3$ **8.** $y = \dfrac{4}{x} - 3x + x^2$

Find the gradients of the following curves at the given points:

9. $y = 2x^2$, $(-1, 2)$ **10.** $y = x^3 - 5x + 2$, $(2, 0)$

11. $y = 4 + \dfrac{6}{x}$, $(3, 6)$ **12.** $y = 3x^2 - 6 - \dfrac{8}{x^2}$, $(-2, 4)$

13. $y = \frac{1}{4}(8 - x - x^2)$, $(-4, -1)$

14. $y = 3x^2 + x - 5$, $(\frac{2}{3}, -3)$

15. Find the gradient of the curve $y = x^3 + x + 1$ at the point $(1, 3)$. At what other point has the curve this same gradient?

16. Find the point on the curve $y = 2x - 3x^2$ at which the tangent is parallel to the x axis.

17. Find the gradient of the curve $xy = 6$ at the points $(2, 3)$ and $(-3, -2)$.

18. Find the point on the curve $y = \frac{1}{2}x^2 - x + 5$ at which the tangent is parallel to the line $y = 2x$.

19. Sketch the curve $y = \frac{1}{4}x^2$ and calculate the gradient at P $(6, 9)$. The tangent at P meets the x axis at Q and the y axis at R. Calculate the co-ordinates of the mid-point of QR.

20. Sketch the curve $y = 5x - x^2$.

Find the gradient of the curve at A $(3, 6)$.

If the tangent at the point B is perpendicular to the tangent at A, find the co-ordinates of B.

MAXIMA AND MINIMA

Exercise 26

Find the maximum and minimum values of:

1. $10x - x^2$ **2.** $3 - 4x - x^2$ **3.** $3x^2 - 2x + 5$

4. $x + \dfrac{4}{x}$ **5.** $x^3 - 12x + 5$ **6.** $4x^3 + 3x^2 - 6x + 3$

7. Find the turning points on the curve
$$y = x^3 - 3x^2 - 9x + 10.$$
Sketch the curve showing these points and the point where the curve cuts the y-axis.

8. The perimeter of a rectangle is 24 cm. Find the maximum area of the rectangle.

9. The sum of two numbers is 12. Find the minimum value of the sum of their squares.

10. A square of side x cm is cut from each corner of a square sheet of cardboard of side 30 cm and the cardboard is folded to form an open box of volume V cm³. Express V in terms of x and find the value of x for which V is a minimum.

11. The skeleton of a rectangular block is to be made from 96 cm of wire. If the width of the block is x cm and the length is $3x$ cm, find the height and show that the volume is $12x^2 (6 - x)$ cm³.

Find the value of x for which the volume is a maximum.

12. A piece of wire of length 40 cm is cut into eight pieces which are used to form a square and a rectangle. The length of the rectangle is three times its width. Taking the width as x cm and the sum of the two areas as A cm², express A in terms of x.

Calculate the value of x for which A is a minimum.

13. A straight line through the point (2, 4) has the equation $(y - 4) + k(x - 2) = 0$. If it cuts the positive x axis at A and the positive y axis at B find, in terms of k, the lengths of OA and OB and the area of triangle OAB.

Calculate the minimum area of the triangle.

INTEGRATION

Integrate:

1. x^2, $12x$, $\dfrac{1}{x^2}$, $\dfrac{6}{x^3}$

2. $1 + x + x^2$ **3.** $6x - 8$ **4.** $\dfrac{6}{x^2} - 6x^2$

5. $\frac{2}{3}x - \frac{1}{4}x^2$ **6.** $x(x^3 - 2x + 5)$ **7.** $(1 - x^2)(2 + x)$

Evaluate:

8. $\displaystyle\int (7x + 3)dx$ **9.** $\displaystyle\int (4x^3 - 12x^2)dx$ **10.** $\displaystyle\int \dfrac{x^4 - 3}{x^2}\, dx$

11. If $\dfrac{dy}{dx} = 12x^2$ and $y = 1\frac{1}{2}$ when $x = -\frac{1}{2}$, find y.

12. If $\dfrac{dy}{dx} = 4x^3 + 6x^2 + 6x + 1$ and $y = 2$ when $x = 1$, find y when $x = -1$.

13. The gradient of a curve which passes through $(1, -1)$ is $3x^2 - 10x$. Find the equation of the curve. Find also the x co-ordinates of the points at which the gradient is 8.

14. The gradient of a curve is given by $\dfrac{dy}{dx} = 2x - 6$. If the minimum value of y is -1, find the equation of the curve and the co-ordinates of the points where it cuts the x axis.

15. The gradient of a curve is given by $\dfrac{dy}{dx} = 6x(x - 1)$. If the curve passes through $(1, 3)$ find its equation.

Find the point on the curve at which the tangent is parallel to the tangent at $(2, 8)$.

Sketch the curve and the two tangents.

AREAS AND VOLUMES

Exercise 28

Evaluate:

1. $\int_2^3 x^2 dx$ **2.** $\int_1^4 \frac{1}{x^2}\, dx$ **3.** $\int_{-1}^2 (2x + 3)dx$

4. $\int_{-1}^1 (3x^2 + 7x - 2)dx$ **5.** $\int_{-2}^1 (3 - 5x)dx$

6. $\int_{-a}^{2a} (x^2 + a^2)dx$

7. Find the area under the curve $y = 3x^2 + 4x$ between $x = 1$ and $x = 3$.

8. Find the area bounded by the curve $y = 2 + \frac{1}{x^2}$, the x axis and the ordinates $x = 2$ and $x = 4$.

9. Find the area between the curve $y = (2 - x)(1 + x)$ and the x axis.

10. Find the area between the curve $y = x - x^2$ and the x axis.

11. Sketch the curve $y = x(5 - x)$ and the line $y = x$. Calculate the area between them.

12. The sketch shows the graphs of $y = 8x - x^2 - 7$ and $y = x + 3$.

Find the co-ordinates of A, B, C and D.

Calculate the area between the curve and the straight line.

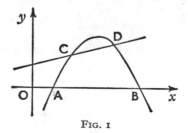

Fig. 1

Questions 13 to 16: Find the volume of the solid of revolution formed by revolving about the x axis the area between the given curve, the x axis and the two ordinates stated. Leave the answers in terms of π.

13. $y = x^2$; $x = 1, x = 2$ **14.** $y = \dfrac{1}{x}$; $x = 1, x = 3$

15. $y = 3x + 2$; $x = 0, x = 2$

16. $y = \sqrt{4 - x^2}$; $x = -1, x = 1$

17. Sketch the curve $y = x^2 - x$. Calculate the volume formed by rotating about the x axis the area between the curve and that axis.

18. Sketch the curve $y = 4 - x^2$ and calculate the volume of the solid formed by rotating about the x axis the area between the curve, the y axis and the positive part of the x axis. Calculate the ratio of the two parts into which the volume is divided by the plane formed by rotating the ordinate $x = 1$.

VELOCITY, ACCELERATION AND OTHER RATES OF CHANGE

EXERCISE 29

Questions 1 to 8: A body is moving along a straight line. After t seconds its distance from a fixed point on the line is s metres, its velocity is v m/s and its acceleration is f m/s^2.

1. $s = 9t - t^2$. Find v when $t = 2$ and s when $v = 1$.

2. $v = 3t^2 + 4t$. Find f when $t = 1$ and when $t = 3$.

3. $s = 5 + 27t - t^3$. Find t when $v = 0$ and find s for that value of t.

4. $v = 4t + 3$. Find s, given that $s = 0$ when $t = 0$.

5. $f = 6t - 4$. Find s, given that when $t = 0$, $v = 3$ and $s = 0$.

6. $v = 6t(t - 1)$. Calculate the distance moved in the first four seconds and the distance moved in the fourth second.

7. $s = 3t + 4t^2$. Find the velocity after 2 s. Find the time at which the velocity is 15 m/s and the distance from the fixed point at that time.

8. $v = ct^2$. Find c if $s = 54$ when $t = 6$ and $s = 0$ when $t = 0$. Find t when $s = 128$ and also v and f for that value of t.

9. The volume, V cm³, of liquid in a vessel after t min is given by $V = 400 + 100t - 20t^2$. Find the rate at which the volume is changing when $t = 1\frac{1}{2}$ and when $t = 3$.

10. The pressure and volume of a gas are connected by the formula $pv = 900$. Find the rate of change of p with respect to v.

11. Find the formula for the total surface area, A cm², of a solid cylinder of height 6 cm and radius r cm. Find the rate of change of A with respect to r when $r = 3$.

12. A body starts from rest at P and comes to rest again at Q. Its velocity, v m/s, t s after leaving P is given by $v = 9t - t^2$. Calculate (i) its initial acceleration, (ii) its maximum velocity between P and Q, (iii) the time taken from P to Q, (iv) the distance PQ.

13. The acceleration of a particle moving in a straight line is $(4 - 6t)$ m/s² at t s after passing point A. When $t = 3$ the particle is momentarily at rest. Find expressions for the velocity and distance from A at time t and find the speed with which it arrives back at A.

14. The velocity of a particle moving in a straight line is $(3t^2 - 7t)$ m/s at t s after leaving point P. At Q the velocity is 20 m/s. The particle takes the same time from Q to R as from P to Q. Find (i) the velocity at R, (ii) the distances PQ and QR, (iii) the acceleration at Q and at R.

ANGLES

Properties of angles at a point and angles made with parallel lines.

The exterior angle property and angle-sum of a triangle.

Angle-sum properties of polygons.

The isosceles triangle.

EXERCISE 30

Calculate all the unknown angles in the following figures:

1.

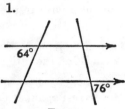

FIG. 2

2.

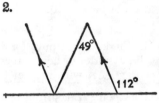

FIG. 3

3.

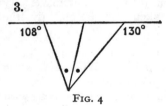

FIG. 4

4.

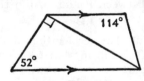

FIG. 5

5.

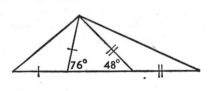

FIG. 6

6.

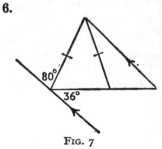

FIG. 7

44

Calculate the values of the letters in the following figures:

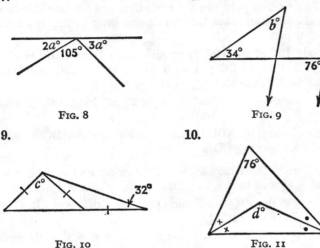

7.

2*a*° 105° 3*a*°

FIG. 8

8.

b°

34°

76°

FIG. 9

9.

c°

32°

FIG. 10

10.

76°

d°

FIG. 11

11. Calculate the exterior angle of a regular polygon with (*a*) 8, (*b*) 12, (*c*) 20 sides.

12. Calculate the interior angle of a regular polygon with (*a*) 10, (*b*) 9, (*c*) 16 sides.

13. Is it possible to have a regular polygon with an exterior angle of (*a*) 40°, (*b*) 50°, (*c*) 10°, (*d*) 80°, (*e*) 24°? Where it is possible, state the number of sides.

14. Is it possible to have a regular polygon with an interior angle of (*a*) 160°, (*b*) 168°, (*c*) 145° (*d*) 157½°? Where it is possible, state the number of sides.

15. A hexagon has angles of 88°, 106°, 123°, 137° and 118°. Calculate the sixth angle.

16. The angles of a pentagon are *x*, *x* + 16, *x* − 10, 2*x* − 35 and 104 degrees. Calculate *x*.

17. ABCDE is a regular pentagon. Calculate the angles of △ ABD. If AC and BD intersect at H, calculate ∠ AHB.

18. Two regular polygons are such that one has one side more than the other and their interior angles differ by 5°. How many sides has each?

19. Side BA of △ ABC is produced to D and the bisector of ∠ CAD meets BC produced at E. If ∠ ABC = 40° and ∠AEC = 22°, calculate ∠ ACB.

20. In isosceles △ ABC, ∠ A = 2∠B. Find two possible sizes for ∠ C.

21. Equilateral △ ABE is drawn inside square ABCD. Calculate the angles of △ CDE.

22. AB and CD are parallel lines. The bisector of ∠ BAC meets CD at E. Prove that AC = CE.

23. In △ PQR, ∠ Q = 90° and QT is the altitude to PR. Prove that ∠ PQT = ∠PRQ.

24. In △ FGH, FG = FH and the bisector of ∠ FGH meets FH at K. Prove that ∠ FKG = 3 ∠ HGK.

25. The sides AQ and BP of △s ABP and ABQ intersect at R; AP is parallel to BQ. Prove that ∠ PRQ = ∠ APB + ∠ AQB.

26. CE is drawn parallel to side BA of △ ABC and equal to side BC. Prove that BE bisects ∠ ABC.

27. From the mid-point M of line PQ, a line MR is drawn equal to ½ PQ. Prove that ∠ PRQ = 90°.

28. The bisectors of ∠ E and ∠ F of △ DEF meet at P; a line through P parallel to EF meets DE and DF at Q and R. Prove that EQ + FR = QR.

29. The sides AB, AC of △ ABC are produced to D, E; the bisectors of ∠ CBD and ∠ BCE meet at I. Prove that ∠ BAC + 2∠ BIC = 180°.

30. In △ ABC, ∠ A = 90°. The bisector of ∠ ABC meets AC at P; the perpendicular from A to BC cuts BP at Q. Prove that △ APQ is isosceles.

CONGRUENCY AND SIMILARITY OF TRIANGLES

1. In $\triangle$ ABC, $\angle$ A = 53°, $\angle$ C = 40°, BC = 4 cm, AC = 5 cm.

Which of the following triangles are (i) congruent to $\triangle$ ABC, (ii) similar to $\triangle$ ABC? Give reasons.

$\triangle$ DEF: $\angle$ F = 40°, ED = 4 cm, DF = 5 cm
$\triangle$ HIJ: $\angle$ I = 40°, HI = 4 cm, IJ = 5 cm
$\triangle$ LMN: $\angle$ N = 40°, $\angle$ M = 53°, LN = 5 cm
$\triangle$ PQR: $\angle$ R = 40°, $\angle$ Q = 87°, PR = 5 cm
$\triangle$ STV: $\angle$ V = 40°, $\angle$ T = 53°, TV = 4 cm
$\triangle$ XYZ: $\angle$ Y = 40°, XY = 4 m, YZ = 5 m

2. (a) In $\triangle$s ABC, PQR, $\angle$ A = $\angle$ R, $\angle$ C = $\angle$ P, BC = PQ. Name the other pairs of equal sides.

(b) In $\triangle$s DEF, GHJ, $\angle$ D = $\angle$ H, $\angle$ E = $\angle$ G. Complete $\dfrac{DE}{HJ} = \dfrac{\quad}{\quad}$.

3. ABC is an equilateral triangle; P, Q, R are points on AB, BC, CA such that AP = BQ = CR. Prove that $\triangle$ PQR is equilateral.

4. AM is a median of $\triangle$ ABC; BP, CQ are perpendiculars from B, C to AM, produced as necessary. Prove that BP = CQ.

5. PQRS is a square. Using P as centre, an arc of a circle is drawn to cut QR at X and SR at Y. Prove that RX = RY.

6. In $\triangle$ ABC, $\angle$ A = 90° and AN is an altitude. Prove that $\triangle$s ABN and ACN are similar. Hence prove that AN² = BN.NC.

7. Altitudes AD, BE of $\triangle$ ABC intersect at H. Name four similar triangles and state the sides which correspond to DH. If BD = 4 cm, DH = 3 cm, BH = 5 cm, DC = 3½ cm, calculate EC and AH.

8. The diagonals AC and BD of trapezium ABCD (AB ∥ CD) cut at E. Name a pair of similar triangles.

If AB = 4 cm, CD = 6 cm, BE = 5 cm, CE = 7 cm, calculate as many lengths as possible.

9. D is a point on side BC of △ ABC. A line through B parallel to AC meets AD produced at E; a line through D parallel to EB meets AB at F. Name pairs of similar triangles.

If AC = 9 cm, BD = 2 cm, DC = 4 cm, AD = 7 cm, calculate as many lengths as possible.

10. WXYZ is a square; R, S, T are points on WX, XY, YZ such that WR = XS = YT. Prove that RS = ST, ∠ RST = 90° and ∠ RTS = 45°.

11. P is a point on side AB of square ABCD. From B and D perpendiculars BL and DN are drawn to PC. Prove that BL = CN.

By using two similar triangles prove that BL² = PL.LC.

12. The bisectors of ∠ A and ∠ B of △ ABC meet at I. From I perpendiculars IP, IQ, IR are drawn to the sides BC, CA, AB. Prove that (i) IP = IQ = IR, (ii) IC bisects ∠ ACB.

13. ABCD is a trapezium with AB ∥ CD; the bisectors of ∠ B and ∠ C meet at E on AD. Prove that ∠ BEC = 90°. If M is a point on BC such that AB = BM, prove that MC = CD.

14. E is the mid-point of side AB of square ABCD; square DEFG is drawn on the same side of DE as A. Prove that (i) AG = CE, (ii) GA and CE produced meet at right angles.

PARALLELOGRAMS AND OTHER QUADRILATERALS

EXERCISE 32

1. ABCD, ABEF are parallelograms on the same side of AB. Prove that DE and CF bisect each other.

2. The bisectors of ∠ A and ∠ B of par. ABCD meet at P on side CD. Prove that (i) AB = 2 BC, (ii) ∠ APB = 90°.

3. ABCD is a parallelogram; AB is produced to E so that BE = AB; EF is parallel to CA and meets CB produced at F. Prove that AF = EC.

4. ABCD is a parallelogram. The bisectors of $\angle$ A and $\angle$ C meet BD at P and Q. Prove that (i) BP = DQ, (ii) AQ, PC are equal and parallel, (iii) AP, CQ are equal and parallel.

5. State the nature of quadrilateral ABCD if:

   (i) $\angle$ A = $\angle$ B = $\angle$ C = $\angle$ D;
   (ii) $\angle$ A = $\angle$ B and $\angle$ C = $\angle$ D;
   (iii) $\angle$ A = $\angle$ C and $\angle$ B = $\angle$ D;
   (iv) $\angle$ A = $\angle$ C and AB = BC;
   (v) AB = BC = CD = DA;
   (vi) AB = BC and $\angle$ A = $\angle$ B = $\angle$ C = 90°.

6. PQRS is a parallelogram. Name the special parallelogram obtained if (i) PR = QS; (ii) PR is perpendicular to QS; (iii) PR = QS and PR is perpendicular to QS.

7. ABCD is a square; E, F, G, H are points on AB, BC, CD, DA such that AE = BF = CG = DH. Prove that EFGH is a square.

8. In par. PQRS, PR = PQ; X, Y are the mid-points of QR, PS. Prove that YRXP is a rectangle.

9. The diagonals of par. ABCD intersect at O; a line PQRS through O meets DA produced, AB, CD, BC produced at P, Q, R, S. Prove that (i) OQ = OR, (ii) PQ = RS, (iii) AS is equal and parallel to PC.

10. In quad. PQRS, PQ is parallel to RS; QS, RP bisect $\angle$ Q, $\angle$ R and intersect at T. Prove that (i) $\angle$ PTQ = 90°, (ii) PT = TR, (iii) PRQS is a rhombus.

11. $\triangle$ ABC is drawn inside square BCDE; lines BF and CF are drawn parallel to EA and DA to meet at F. Prove that (i) $\triangle$s EAD and BFC are congruent, (ii) AF = BC, and (iii) AF is perpendicular to BC.

12. ABCD is a quadrilateral such that AB is parallel to DC and AC, DB bisect $\angle$ BAD, $\angle$ CDA. Prove that ABCD is a rhombus. BA, CD are produced; the bisectors of the exterior angles formed meet at Q and AC meets BD at P. Prove that PQ = AD.

EQUAL INTERCEPTS

EXERCISE 33

1. D, E, F, G are points on side AB of $\triangle$ ABC such that AD = DE = EF = FG = GB. Lines through D, E, F, G parallel to BC meet AC at P, Q, R, S. If AC = 7 cm, calculate PR.

2. P is the mid-point of side BC of $\triangle$ ABC; PQ is drawn parallel to CA to meet AB at Q and QR is drawn parallel to AP to meet BC at R. Prove that BC = 4 BR.

3. E, F are the mid-points of sides AC, AB of $\triangle$ ABC; BE, CF are produced to meet at P, Q the line through A parallel to BC. Prove that A is the mid-point of PQ.

4. ABCD is a quadrilateral; P, Q, R, S are the mid-points of AB, BC, CD, DA. Prove that (i) PS is parallel and equal to RQ, (ii) PR and QS bisect each other.

5. ABCD is a parallelogram; E is the mid-point of AB; BF is drawn parallel to ED intersecting DC at G and meeting AD produced at F. Prove that (i) FD = BC, (ii) BDFC is a parallelogram.

6. PQRS is a parallelogram; L, M are the mid-points of PQ, RS. Prove that (i) LQMS is a parallelogram, (ii) LS and MQ trisect PR.

7. E is the mid-point of side AC of $\triangle$ ABC; EF is drawn parallel to BC to meet AB at F; L, M are the mid-points of FC, BC. Prove that E, L, M are colinear and that EL = LM.

8. The medians BP, CQ of $\triangle$ ABC intersect at R; AR is produced to S so that AR = RS. Prove that (i) BRCS is a parallelogram, (ii) R is a point of trisection of BP.

ELEMENTARY CONSTRUCTIONS

Bisection of angles and straight lines; construction of perpendiculars to a given line and of angles equal to a given angle; angles of 60°, 30°, 90°, 45°; triangles and quadrilaterals; division of a straight line into a number of equal parts or in a given ratio.

EXERCISE 34

Do NOT use a protractor in Questions 1 to 9.

1. Draw $\triangle$ ABC given that AB = 8 cm, BC = 7 cm, $\angle$ B = 60°. Construct the bisectors of the three angles. Let the bisector of $\angle$ A meet BC at P. Measure AP.

2. Draw $\triangle$ GHK having GH = 5 cm, GK = 6 cm, $\angle$ HGK = 120°. Construct the perpendicular bisectors of GH and GK. If they meet at L, measure GL.

3. Construct $\triangle$ PQR given that PQ = 8 cm, QR = 9 cm, RP = 7.5 cm. Construct the three altitudes and measure them.

4. Draw $\triangle$ ABC having AC = BC = 6 cm, AB = 4 cm. Through A construct AD parallel to BC and from C construct a line perpendicular to AD meeting it at E. Measure CE.

5. Draw $\triangle$ PQR having PQ = 4.6 cm, QR = 5.6 cm, RP = 3.8 cm. Construct $\triangle$ XYZ having $\angle$ Y = $\angle$ Q, $\angle$ Z = $\angle$ R, YZ = 4.6 cm. Measure XY.

6. Construct angles of $22\frac{1}{2}$° and 75°.

7. Draw a line of length 8.2 cm and divide it into five equal parts.

8. Draw a line AB of length 9.8 cm. Find a point P on AB such that AP : PB = 4 : 3. Measure AP.

9. Construct the trapezium HKLM in which HK is parallel to ML, HK = 4 cm, KL = 6 cm, LM = 8 cm, $\angle$ HKL = 120°. Construct the perpendicular from H to ML and measure it.

10. $\triangle$ EBC has base BC on line ABCD; AB = BE and EC = CD; $\angle$ EBC = 60° and $\angle$ ECB = 70°. Calculate $\angle$ EAB and $\angle$ EDC. Hence construct $\triangle$ EBC given that its perimeter is 12 cm. Measure BC.

SINE, COSINE AND TANGENT OF AN ACUTE ANGLE

EXERCISE 35

Questions 1 to 5: In $\triangle$ ABC, $\angle$ B = 90°.

1. If AB = 8 cm, $\angle$ A = 28°, calculate BC.

2. If AB = 12 cm, BC = 5 cm, calculate $\angle$ A.

3. If AC = 6 cm, $\angle$ A = 28°, calculate BC.

4. If AC = 9 cm, $\angle$ A = 56°, calculate AB.

5. If BC = 11 cm, AC = 15 cm, calculate $\angle$ C.

6. From the top of a cliff of height 120 m, the angle of depression of a boat is 33° 36′. Calculate the distance of the boat from the cliff.

7. A chord of length 10 cm subtends an angle of 156° at the centre of a circle. Calculate its distance from the centre.

8. The diagonals of a rhombus have lengths of 18 cm and 12 cm. Calculate the acute angle of the rhombus.

9. An isosceles triangle has sides of 6 cm and an angle of 52° at the apex. Calculate the base.

10. Calculate the angle subtended at the centre of a circle of radius 4.5 cm by a chord of length 7.2 cm.

11. B is 8 km east of A, C is 6 km south of B, D is 4 km east of C. Calculate the bearing of D from A.

12. If sin A = 0.4 and cos B = 0.8, find sin(A + B) and cos(A + B).

13. If sin P = 0.8 and sin Q = 0.6, find sin(P − Q).

14. If sin θ = 2 sin 28° 30′, find θ.

15. The sides of a rectangle are 6.4 cm and 8.0 cm. Calculate the obtuse angle between the diagonals.

16. In △ ABC, AB = 8 cm, ∠ B = 90°, BC = 12 cm. M is the mid-point of BC. Calculate ∠ BAM and ∠ MAC.

17. In △ DEF, ∠ D = 50°, ∠ E = 90°, EF = 8 cm. Calculate DF.

18. In quad. ABCD, ∠ A = ∠ D = 90°, AB = 4 cm, DC = 7 cm, ∠ C = 65°. Calculate BC.

19. If $\mu = \dfrac{\sin i}{\sin r}$, (i) find μ if i = 54° and r = 33°; (ii) find r if i = 47° and μ = 1.5.

20. In △ ABC, AB = 4 cm, ∠ B = 32°, ∠ C = 54°; AN is an altitude. Calculate AN and CN.

21. An eight-sided regular polygon has a side of 8 cm. Calculate (i) the radius of the circumcircle; (ii) the distance of the circumcentre from a side; (iii) the area of the polygon.

22. In △ ABC, ∠ B = 35°, ∠ C = 90°; D is a point on BC; BD = 8 cm and ∠ ADC = 70°. Calculate DC and AC.

23. A man standing 20 m from a tower measures the angles of elevation of the top and bottom of a flagstaff on the tower as 58° and 55°. Calculate the height of the flagstaff, to the nearest 0.1 m.

24. A pendulum of length 2 m is attached to a point 3 m from the floor. It swings through 35° each side of the vertical. Calculate its height from the floor at the ends of its path and the horizontal distance between the ends.

25. In quad. ABCD, AB = 8 cm, BC = 6 cm, CD = DA = 7 cm, ∠ B = 90°. Calculate AC and the angles of the quadrilateral.

26. Q is 4 km east of P. A ship leaves P at 2 p.m. and sails due south at 24 km/h; another ship leaves Q at 2.30 p.m. and sails south-east at 20 km/h. Calculate the distance and bearing of the second ship from the first at 2.45 p.m.

27. A, B, C are three points on the bank of a river and P is the point on the bank directly opposite C. If AB = 50 m, ∠ PAB = 20°, ∠ PBC = 40°, calculate BC and PC.

28. Town B is 150 km from aerodrome A in the direction 157°. An aeroplane flies from A on a course of 140°. Find (i) its shortest distance from B; (ii) its distance from B when it is due east of it.

29. In Fig. 12, if AC = 6 cm, calculate CE and DE.

30. A hollow cone of semi-vertical angle 20° is placed with its vertex in contact with a horizontal plane and its axis at 60° to the plane. A sphere of radius 6 cm is placed inside the cone. Calculate the height of the centre of the sphere above the plane.

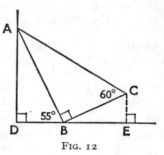

FIG. 12

AREA PROPERTIES OF TRIANGLES AND PARALLELOGRAMS

EXERCISE 36

1. In △ ABC, AB = 10 cm, BC = 9 cm, altitude AD = 8 cm. Calculate (i) the area of △ ABC and (ii) altitude CF.

2. In par. PQRS, PT and PV are the perpendiculars from P to QR and SR. If PT = 6 cm, PV = 5 cm and the area of PQRS is 24 cm², calculate PQ and QR.

3. In △ DEF, EF = 6 cm, FD = 10 cm, ∠ F = 48°. Calculate the area.

4. Find the area of a rhombus having sides of 9.5 cm and two angles of 76°.

5. Calculate the angles of a parallelogram having sides of 5.2 cm and 8.4 cm and an area of 28.6 cm².

6. A triangle has an area of 12 cm² and two sides of 8 cm and 6 cm. Calculate the angle between these sides.

7. Calculate the area of a triangle having sides of 6, 9 and 11 cm.

8. Calculate the area of a triangle having sides of 7.8, 6.6 and 10.4 cm.

9. A regular pentagon ABCDE is inscribed in a circle, centre O, radius 6 cm. Calculate the area of (i) $\triangle$ OAB, (ii) the pentagon.

10. P, Q are the mid-points of sides KL, LM of par. KLMO. If the area of KLMO is 60 cm², calculate the area of $\triangle$ OPQ.

11. In $\triangle$ ABC, $\angle$ B = 90°, AB = 12 cm, BC = 9 cm; P, Q are points on AB, AC such that AP = 2PB and AQ = $\frac{1}{2}$ QC. Calculate the area of $\triangle$ APQ.

12. A triangle has a base $\frac{3}{4}$ that of a parallelogram and a height $\frac{2}{3}$ that of the parallelogram. Express the area of the triangle as a fraction of that of the parallelogram.

13. The area of $\triangle$ ABC is 70 cm²; D is a point on BC such that BD : DC = 3 : 2 and E is a point on AD such that AE : ED = 4 : 3. Calculate the areas of $\triangle$ ADC and $\triangle$ EDC.

14. G, H are points on the sides KL, LM of $\triangle$ KLM such that KG : GL = 1 : 2 and LH : HM = 1 : 3. Express the areas of (i) $\triangle$ LGM, (ii) $\triangle$ GHM, (iii) quad. KGHM as fractions of the area of $\triangle$ KLM.

15. Sides AB, BC, CA of $\triangle$ ABC are produced to D, E, F so that BD = AB, CE = 2BC, AF = 3CA. If the area of $\triangle$ ABC is x cm², find the area of $\triangle$ DEF.

16. In quad. ABCD, AB is parallel to CD; the diagonals intersect at O. Prove that $\triangle$s AOD and COB are equal in area.

17. Diagonal EG of par. EFGH is produced to K so that GK = EG. Prove that △ EFK = par. EFGH.

18. T is any point on side QR of par. PQRS. ST produced meets PQ produced at V. Prove that △ PST = △ SRV.

19. L is any point on median AM of △ ABC. Prove that △ ABL = △ ACL.

20. P is a point on side HG of par. EFGH; FQ is drawn through F parallel to EP to meet HG produced at Q; QR is drawn through Q parallel to FP to meet EP produced at R. Prove that par. PFQR = par. EFGH.

21. P, Q are the mid-points of sides AB, AC of △ ABC; PC, BQ cut at R. Without joining PQ, prove that (i) △ AQB = △ APC, (ii) quad. APRQ = △ BRC.

22. O is any point on diagonal BD of par. ABCD; lines through O parallel to AB, AD meet AB, BC, CD, DA at P, Q, R, S. Prove that par. APOS = par. OQCR.

AREA CONSTRUCTIONS

A triangle equal in area to a given quadrilateral.
A square equal in area to a given rectangle.

EXERCISE 37

1. Draw a quad. ABCD with AB = 6 cm, BC = 3.4 cm, CD = 4 cm, DA = 5.2 cm, ∠ BAD = 60°. Find a point P on AB produced such that △ APD is equal in area to quad. ABCD. Measure AP.

2. Construct a rectangle having sides of 8 cm and 3.5 cm. Construct a square equal in area to the rectangle and measure its side.

3. Draw a triangle having sides of 9 cm, 8 cm, 7 cm. Construct (i) a rectangle having the same area, (ii) a square having the same area. Measure the side of the square.

4. Construct a line of length $\sqrt{21}$ cm.

5. Construct a rhombus having sides of 8 cm and an area of 48 cm². Measure the acute angle.

Construct also an isosceles triangle having a side of the rhombus as base and an area equal to that of the rhombus.

6. Construct $\triangle$ ABC having AB = AC, BC = 5.2 cm, altitude AD = 7.6 cm. Construct $\triangle$ ABP having $\angle$ BAP = 90° and having the same area as $\triangle$ ABC. Measure BP.

7. Draw quad. ABCD in which AB = 5 cm, BC = 6 cm, CD = 6 cm, DA = 4 cm, $\angle$ DAB = 90°. Construct $\triangle$ BCP equal in area to ABCD and with P on CD produced. Find a point Q on CD such that the area of $\triangle$ BCQ is equal to half that of ABCD. Measure CQ.

OBTUSE ANGLES

Exercise 38

1. Use tables to evaluate:

    (i) sin 108°   (ii) cos 145°   (iii) tan 124°
   (iv) sin 154° 18′   (v) cos 98° 40′   (vi) tan 165° 50′
 (vii) cos 142° 22′ (viii) cos 112° 15′

2. Evaluate:

    (i) $\sin^{-1}$ 0.8910   (ii) $\sin^{-1}$ 0.5693
   (iii) $\cos^{-1}$ 0.5358   (iv) $\cos^{-1}(-0.5358)$
    (v) $\cos^{-1}(-0.7960)$ (vi) $\tan^{-1}(-2.6629)$
 (vii) $\tan^{-1}$ 0.6698   (viii) $\tan^{-1}(-0.3033)$

3. If cos $x = -0.4384$, find sin x and tan x.

4. If tan $x = 2.1445$, find cos x and cos $2x$.

5. If sin $x = 0.9426$ and x is acute, find tan x and tan $2x$.

6. If sin $x = 0.9426$ and x is obtuse, find tan x and tan $\frac{1}{2}x$.

7. If cos $2x = -0.2756$, find cos x and cos $3x$.

8. If sin $3x = 0.9781$, find two possible values of x, cos $4x$ and tan $5x$.

9. Find the area of $\triangle$ ABC if BC $= 3.5$ cm, CA $= 2.4$ cm and $\angle$ C $= 102°$.

10. The area of $\triangle$ PQR is 54 cm². If PQ $= 18$ cm and RP $= 12$ cm, find two possible values of $\angle$ P.

THE SINE FORMULA

EXERCISE 39

1. In $\triangle$ ABC, $b = 4.2$, $\angle$ A $= 72°$, $\angle$ B $= 53°$. Find a.

2. In $\triangle$ ABC, $a = 14.6$, $\angle$ A $= 62°$, $\angle$ C $= 87°$. Find b.

3. In $\triangle$ ABC, $c = 72$, $\angle$ B $= 55°$, $\angle$ C $= 108°$. Find b.

4. In $\triangle$ DEF, $e = 185$, $\angle$ D $= 122°$, $\angle$ F $= 36°$. Find d.

5. In $\triangle$ PQR, $p = 9.16$, $\angle$ P $= 38° 29'$, $\angle$ R $= 74° 15'$. Find r.

6. Calculate the circumradius of $\triangle$ ABC of Question 1.

7. Calculate the circumradius of $\triangle$ ABC of Question 3.

8. A triangle has angles of 75°, 55° and 50° and a circumradius of 15. Calculate its shortest side.

9. The circumradius of $\triangle$ DEF is 8 and $\angle$ D $= 62°$. Calculate EF.

Questions 10, 11, 12: Solve the triangles (i.e. find the unknown sides and angles):

10. $\triangle$ PQR: $p = 8.2$, $\angle$ P $= 52°$, $\angle$ R $= 84°$.

11. $\triangle$XYZ: $y = 236$, $\angle$ X $= 123°$, $\angle$ Y $= 37°$.

12. $\triangle$ DEF: $f = 3.5$, $\angle$ D $= 69° 24'$, $\angle$ E $= 57° 12'$.

13. A and B are points 80 m apart on the bank of a straight section of a river; P is a point on the opposite bank; $\angle$ BAP = 75° and $\angle$ ABP = 65°. Calculate AP and the width of the river.

14. A ship was steaming at 12 knots on a course N. 65° E. At 2 p.m. a lighthouse was observed in the direction S. 44° E.; at 3.15 p.m. the lighthouse was in the direction S. 30° W. Calculate (i) the distance of the ship from the lighthouse at 2 p.m., (ii) the time at which the ship was nearest to the lighthouse.

15. From two points A and B in a horizontal straight line ABC, the angles of elevation of the top T of a tower TC are 14° and 19°. If AB = 40 m, find BT and the height of the tower.

16. P and Q are points on a coast such that Q is 4 km from P in the direction S. 33° W. From a ship R the directions of P and Q are S. 72° E. and S. 28° E. Calculate RP and RQ.

17. An aircraft leaves P at noon and flies at 400 km/h on a course of 150°. At 12.30 p.m. it changes its course to 230°. When is it due south of P and how far is it then from P?

PYTHAGORAS' THEOREM

EXERCISE 40

1. In $\triangle$ ABC, $\angle$ A = 90°. Calculate a if (i) $b = 6$, $c = 8$, (ii) $b = 12$, $c = 5$, (iii) $b = 35$, $c = 12$.

2. In $\triangle$ PQR, $\angle$ P = 90°. Calculate q if (i) $p = 17$, $r = 8$, (ii) $p = 15$, $r = 9$, (iii) $p = 65$, $r = 33$.

3. In $\triangle$ XYZ, $\angle$ X = 90°. (i) If $y = 8$ and $z = 11$, find x. (ii) If $x = 18$ and $y = 7$, find z. [Both to 3 sig. fig.]

4. In quad. ABCD, AB = 20, BC = 15, CD = 24, $\angle$ B = $\angle$ D = 90°. Using diagonal AC, calculate AD.

5. Calculate, correct to 3 sig. fig., the diagonal of a square of side 5 cm.

6. Calculate the longest altitude of a triangle having sides of 16 cm, 17 cm, and 17 cm. Hence find the area.

7. The sides of a rhombus are of length 5 cm. If the length of one diagonal is 9.6 cm, find the length of the other.

8. A sphere of radius 6.5 cm is placed in a circular hole of radius 2.5 cm on a horizontal table. Calculate the height of the top of the sphere above the table.

9. ABC is an equilateral triangle of side 4 cm; BC is produced to D so that CD is 3 cm. Calculate AD.

10. The sides of a triangle are 7.2 cm, 15.3 cm and 13.5 cm. Prove that one angle is a right angle.

11. In trapezium PQRS, $\angle$ P = $\angle$ Q = 90°, PQ = 22 cm, QR = 8 cm, SP = 15 cm, T is a point on PQ such that PT = 10 cm. Find, in surd form, the lengths of TR, TS and RS. Hence prove that $\angle$ RTS = 90°.

12. AD is an altitude of $\triangle$ ABC; AB = 7 cm, BC = 8 cm, CA = 9 cm. Calculate DC.

13. In $\triangle$ PQR, RT = 9 cm, PT = 16 cm, altitude QT = 12 cm. Prove that $\angle$ PQR = 90°.

14. A rope TP of length 7.8 m is tied to the top of a vertical pole TN and to a peg P on the ground 3 m from N. If the rope is shortened by 30 cm, how far must the peg be moved in? What angle does the rope now make with the horizontal?

15. (*a*) A rhombus has sides of length x cm and diagonals of lengths y cm and z cm. Express z in terms of x and y.

(*b*) Prove that a triangle having sides of $2p$, $p^2 - 1$, $p^2 + 1$ units has a right angle.

16. In quad. ABCD, $\angle$ ABC = $\angle$ACD = 90°. Prove that $AD^2 = AB^2 + BC^2 + CD^2$.

17. In $\triangle$ APQ, $\angle$ A = 90°; X, Y are points on AP, AQ. Prove that $PQ^2 + XY^2 = PY^2 + QX^2$.

18. In $\triangle$ ABC, $\angle$ B = 90°; P, Q are the mid-points of BC, AB. Prove that $4(AP^2 + CQ^2) = 5AC^2$.

19. In quad. ABCD, $\angle$ B = 90° and $AB^2 + BC^2 = CD^2 + DA^2$. Prove that $\angle$ D = 90°.

20. P is any point inside $\triangle$ ABC; PL, PM, PN are the perpendiculars from P to BC, CA, AB. Prove that $AN^2 + BL^2 + CM^2 = AM^2 + CL^2 + BN^2$.

21. The side PQ of square PQRS is produced to T. Prove that $ST^2 - RT^2 = PQ^2 + 4\triangle QRT$.

22. A, B, C are fixed points and $\angle$ ABC = 90°. P is a variable point such that $PC^2 - PA^2 = AB^2 + BC^2$. Prove that the locus of P is a straight line through A.

23. OABCD is a right pyramid on a square base ABCD; altitude OE is equal to AB. Prove that $2OA^2 = 3AB^2$. If T is a point of trisection of AB, prove that $18OT^2 = 23AB^2$.

Tables must NOT be used in the following questions. The formula $\sin^2 \theta + \cos^2 \theta = 1$ is required.

24. If $\cos A = \frac{3}{5}$, find $\sin A$ and $\tan A$.

25. If $\sin B = \frac{8}{17}$ and B is obtuse, find $\cos B$ and $\tan B$.

26. If $\cos C = -\frac{7}{25}$, find $\sin C$ and $\tan C$.

27. If $12 \tan D = 5$, find $3 \sin D + 2 \cos D$.

28. If $3 \cos E + 2 = 0$, find $\sin^2 E$ and $1 + \tan^2 E$.

29. If $\tan F = \frac{21}{20}$, find $\sin (90° - F)$, $\sin (180° - F)$ and $\cos (180° - F)$.

30. If $\sin P = \frac{4}{5}$ and $\cos Q = \frac{3}{5}$, write down a connection between A and B (i) if both are acute, (ii) if one is obtuse.

31. Using surds write down the values of:
    (i) sin 45°, sin 135°, cos 135°;
    (ii) sin 60°, cos 120°, tan 120°;
    (iii) sin 30°, sin 150°, tan 150°.

32. Find θ if (i) cos $\theta = \frac{1}{2}$, (ii) cos $\theta = -\frac{1}{2}$, (iii) tan $\theta = 1$, (iv) sin $\theta = \frac{\sqrt{3}}{2}$.

33. Evaluate: $1 - \cos^2 30°$; $1 - \sin^2 45°$.

34. Simplify: $1 - \cos^2\theta$; $5 \sin^2\theta + 2 \cos^2\theta$.

35. Evaluate: $\sin^2 120° - \cos^2 120°$; $(\tan 45° + \cos 60°) \div \sin^2 60°$.

36. Evaluate: sin 45° cos 45°; sin 30° cos 30°; tan 60° cos 30°.

37. Evaluate: $\dfrac{\cos 60°}{\sin 30°}$; $\dfrac{\tan 60°}{\tan 45°}$; $\dfrac{\tan 30°}{\tan 60°}$; $\dfrac{\tan 45°}{\cos 60°}$.

38. Find θ if (i) $\tan^2\theta = 3$, (ii) $4 \cos^2\theta = 3$.

39. The longest side of a 30° — 60° set square is 14 cm. Calculate the lengths of the other two sides.

40. A rhombus has a side of 10 cm and two angles of 60°. Calculate the lengths of the diagonals.

41. In $\triangle$ ABC, AB = 6 cm, $\angle$ B = 30°, $\angle$ C = 45°. By using altitude AD, prove that AC = $3\sqrt{2}$ cm and BC = $3(1 + \sqrt{3})$ cm.

THE COSINE FORMULA

EXERCISE 41

1. In $\triangle$ ABC, if $b = 5$, $c = 7$, $\angle$ A = 38°, find a.

2. In $\triangle$ ABC, if $a = 10$, $b = 14$, $\angle$ C = 60°, find c.

3. In $\triangle$ ABC, if $a = 11$, $c = 8$, $\angle$ B = 124°, find b.

4. In $\triangle$ ABC, if $a = 4$, $b = 6$, $c = 5$, find A.

5. In $\triangle$ ABC, if $a = 7$, $b = 10$, $c = 5$, find B.

Questions 6, 7, 8: Solve the triangles:

6. $\triangle$ PQR: $p = 13$, $q = 10$, $r = 15$.

7. $\triangle$ DEF: $d = 8$, $e = 11$, $\angle$ F = 109°.

8. $\triangle$ KLM: $k = 236$, $l = 436$, $m = 269$.

9. A triangle has sides of 7 cm, 5 cm, 3 cm. Calculate the largest angle.

10. A parallelogram has sides of 10 cm and 6 cm and two angles of 136°. Calculate the lengths of the diagonals.

11. A, B, C are three points on a coast. B is 7 km from A in the direction 165°; C is 9 km from B in the direction 215°. Calculate the distance and bearing of C from A.

12. In $\triangle$ PQR, PQ = 4 cm, QR = 6 cm and $\angle$ Q is obtuse. PN is an altitude and QN = 1 cm. State the cosine of $\angle$ PQR and calculate PR without using tables.

13. AOB is a diameter of a circle of radius 3 cm; OD is a radius such that $\angle$ AOD = 120°; OD is produced to P so that DP = 2 cm. Calculate AP, BP and $\angle$ APB.

14. PQRS is a square of side 6 cm; T, V are points on QR, SR such that QT = SV = 2 cm. Prove that cos TPV = $\frac{3}{5}$.

15. From the top T of a tower TM the angles of depression of points A and B are 15° and 20°. A is due south of M and B is south-east of M. If TM = 60 m calculate AM, BM and AB.

THE CIRCLE: CHORDS AND TANGENTS

EXERCISE 42

1. AB is a chord of a circle, centre C, radius 10 cm; CN is the perpendicular to AB. If CN = 8 cm, find AB. If AB = 14 cm, find CN, to 3 sig. fig.

2. Two chords of a circle, radius 6.5 cm, are parallel and have lengths of 12 cm and 10.4 cm. Calculate their distance apart.

3. AB is a chord of a circle, centre O. The tangent at B meets AO produced at T. If $\angle$ BTA = 52°, calculate $\angle$ BAT.

4. A circle touches sides BC, CA, AB of $\triangle$ ABC at D, E, F. If $\angle$ BAC = 42° and $\angle$ BDF = 54°, calculate $\angle$ DFE.

5. (*a*) Calculate the length of the tangent to a circle of radius 9 cm from a point 15 cm from the centre.

(*b*) OA is a radius of a circle and AT is a tangent. If OA = 3.3 cm and AT = 5.6 cm, calculate OT.

6. The radii of two concentric circles are 17 cm and 10 cm; a line ABCD cuts one circle at A, D and the other at B, C. If BC = 12 cm, calculate AB.

7. P is a point on a circle, centre O, radius 3 cm; OP is produced to Q so that PQ = 2 cm. Calculate the lengths of the tangents QS and QR. If RS cuts OP at T, find OT and RS.

8. Two circles, centres P and Q, cut at A and B. A line CAD, drawn parallel to PQ, meets one circle at C and the other at D. Prove that CD = 2PQ.

9. Two chords AB, CD of a circle, centre O, are produced to meet at P. If $\angle$ OPA = $\angle$ OPC, prove that AB = CD.

10. A circle touches the sides BC, CA, AB of $\triangle$ ABC at D, E, F. If D is the mid-point of BC, prove that $\triangle$ ABC is isosceles.

11. The four sides of quad. ABCD touch a circle, centre O. Prove that (i) AB + CD = AD + CB, (ii) $\angle$ AOB + $\angle$ COD = 180°.

12. TA and TB are tangents to a circle. A third tangent touches the circle at C on the minor arc AB and meets TA, TB at P, Q. Prove that the perimeter of $\triangle$ PQT = 2AT.

THE CIRCLE: ANGLE PROPERTIES

1. ABCD is a cyclic quadrilateral; $\angle$ BAC = 63°, $\angle$ ACB = 67°, AD = DC. Calculate $\angle$ ABC, $\angle$ ADC, $\angle$ DAC.

2. PQRS is a cyclic quadrilateral; $\angle$ SPQ = 76°, $\angle$ SQP = 58°. Calculate $\angle$ PRQ and $\angle$ QRS.

3. Side EF of cyclic quad. EFGH is a diameter of the circle. If $\angle$ FEG = x°, write down the values of $\angle$ EFG and $\angle$ EHG.

4. AB is a diameter of a circle; CD is a chord parallel to AB; $\angle$ ADC = 28°. Join AC, AD, BD and calculate all the angles in the figure.

5. The diagonals of cyclic quad. PQRS intersect at V; O is the centre of the circle; $\angle$ POQ = 64°, $\angle$ PVQ = 80°. Find $\angle$ QRP, $\angle$ RQS and $\angle$ ROS.

6. In cyclic quad. ABCD, $\angle$ BAC = 20°, $\angle$ ACB = 32°; O is the centre of the circle and $\angle$ COD = 150°. Calculate $\angle$ BCD and $\angle$ ADC.

7. Sides PQ and SR of cyclic quad. PQRS are produced to meet at T; PS = SR, $\angle$ RPS = 56°, $\angle$ PRQ = 25°. Calculate $\angle$ RQT and $\angle$ QTR.

8. Chord AB of a circle, centre O, is parallel to radius OC; OB and AC intersect at D. If $\angle$ OCD = x°, calculate $\angle$ BDC.

9. P is a point on the minor arc AB of a circle, centre Q. If $\angle$ APB = x° and $\angle$ AQB = y°, express x in terms of y. Calculate x if APBQ is a parallelogram.

10. TA and TB are tangents to a circle, centre C; P is any point on the minor arc AB; $\angle$ ATB = 52°. Calculate $\angle$ ACB and $\angle$ APB.

11. Chords AB, CD of a circle are produced to meet at K. Prove that $\angle$ ADK $=\angle$ CBK. If AD $=$ DK prove that CB $=$ BK.

12. A circle through vertices B and C of $\triangle$ ABC meets sides AB, AC at P, Q. (i) If AB $=$ BC, prove that AQ $=$ PQ. (ii) If AB $=$ AC, prove that PQ is parallel to BC.

13. In cyclic quad. ABCD, AC $=$ AD. If CB is produced to P, prove that AB bisects $\angle$ DBP.

14. ABCD is a cyclic quadrilateral with AB parallel to CD. Prove that $\angle$ C $=\angle$ D. If E is a point on DC and BE is produced to meet the circle at F, prove that $\angle$ DEF $+\angle$ EDF $=\angle$ ABC.

15. In $\triangle$ ABC, AB $=$ AC; D is a point on AB such that CD $=$ BC; CD produced meets the circumcircle of $\triangle$ ABC at E. Prove that (i) AB bisects $\angle$ CAE, (ii) AD $=$ AE.

16. Two circles intersect at A and B; lines CAD, EBF meet one circle at C, E and the other at D, F. Prove that (i) CE is parallel to DF, (ii) $\angle$ EAF $=\angle$ CBD.

17. In cyclic quad. ABCD, AB is parallel to CD; the bisector of $\angle$ A meets CD at E and the circle at F. Prove that EF $=$ CF and that triangles BCF, DEF are congruent.

18. ABCD is a parallelogram. A circle through A cuts AB, AC, AD at P, Q, R. Prove that $\triangle$s PQR, ABC are similar.

19. O is the circumcentre of $\triangle$ ABC; a line through A parallel to BC meets BO produced at P. By joining OC, prove that $\angle$ BAC $+\angle$ APB $=90°$.

20. Two circles, centres O and P, intersect at A and B; a line CAD meets the circles at C and D. If the points O, A, P, B are concyclic, prove that $\angle$ CBD $=90°$.

CONCYCLIC POINTS: ANGLE TESTS

1. In quad. ABCD, AB is parallel to CD. A circle through A and B cuts AD, BC at E, F. Prove that E, D, C, F are concyclic.

2. Chords AXB and CXD of a circle are produced to P and Q so that PQ is parallel to BD. Prove that A, C, P, Q are concyclic.

3. POQ and ROS are straight lines such that PR = PO and SQ = SO. Prove that P, R, Q, S are concyclic.

4. P, Q are the mid-points of chords AB, AC which lie on the same side of the centre O. Prove that A, P, Q, O are concyclic.

5. M is the mid-point of chord AB of a circle, centre O; AB is produced to P and PQ is a tangent to the circle at Q. Prove that ∠ QPB = ∠ MOQ or 180° − ∠ MOQ.

6. X, Y are the mid-points of sides PQ, QR of square PQRS. If PY and SX intersect at Z, prove that (i) ∠ PZX = 90°, (ii) ∠ RZS = ∠ RYS = ∠ PXS.

7. Chord AXB is perpendicular to diameter CXD; lines CEF, CGH meet AB at E, G and the circle at F, H. Prove that EXDF, GXDH, EFHG are cyclic quadrilaterals.

8. The sides AB, AC of △ ABC are produced to E, F; the bisectors of ∠ ABC and ∠ ACB meet at I and the bisectors of ∠ CDE and ∠ BCF meet at K. Prove that (i) B, I, C, K are concyclic, (ii) ∠ BKC = 90° − ½ ∠ BAC.

9. The altitudes AD, BE of △ ABC cut at H.

   (i) Prove that A, E, D, B are concyclic.
   (ii) Prove that H, E, C, D are concyclic.
   (iii) Prove that ∠ CHE = ∠ BAC.
   (iv) If HD is produced to X so that DX = DH, prove that ∠ DBH = ∠ DBX and that A, C, X, B are concyclic.

THE ALTERNATE SEGMENT THEOREM

1. AB is a diameter of a circle; the tangent at C meets AB produced at T. If $\angle$ TCB = 35°, calculate $\angle$ ABC and $\angle$ BTC.

2. PR and QR are tangents at points P and Q on a circle; S is a point on the major arc PQ. If $\angle$ PQS = 78° and $\angle$ QPS = 54°, calculate $\angle$ PRQ.

3. In $\triangle$ ABC, AB = BC and $\angle$ B is obtuse; DAE is the tangent at A to the circumcircle of $\triangle$ ABC and it meets CB produced at E. If $\angle$ DAC = 104°, calculate $\angle$ AEC.

4. A circle touches sides BC, CA, AB of $\triangle$ ABC at P, Q, R; $\angle$ RPQ = 62° and $\angle$ PQR = 48°. Calculate the angles of $\triangle$ ABC.

5. Chord PQ of a circle is produced to R and RT is a tangent. If TQ = QR and $\angle$ QRT = 35°, calculate $\angle$ PQT and $\angle$ PTQ.

6. ABCD is a cyclic quadrilateral; AB is a diameter of the circle, $\angle$ ABD = 42° and $\angle$ CBD = 28°; the tangent at D meets BC produced at E. Calculate $\angle$ BCD and $\angle$ CED.

7. Chord BC of a circle is parallel to the tangent at A. Prove that $\triangle$ ABC is isosceles.

8. Two circles touch a straight line at P and are on the same side of it; two straight lines PQS and PRT meet one circle at Q and R and the other at S and T. Prove that QR is parallel to ST.

9. TA is a tangent to the circumcircle of $\triangle$ ABC. If AB = BC, prove that $\angle$ TAB = $\angle$ BAC or 180° − $\angle$ BAC.

10. Sides SP and RQ of cyclic quad. PQRS are produced to meet at T; VT is a line parallel to SR. Prove that VT is a tangent to the circumcircle of $\triangle$ TPQ.

11. Two circles intersect at A and B; P is a point on one circle and lines PAQ and PBR meet the other circle at Q and R; PT is the tangent at P. If PA bisects $\angle$ BPT, prove that RQ = RP.

12. In $\triangle$ ABC, AB = AC; a circle through A touches BC at B and cuts AC at D. Prove that BD = BC. If also BD bisects $\angle$ ABC, calculate $\angle$ BAC.

13. Diagonals PR and QS of cyclic quad. PQRS intersect at X; the tangent at P is parallel to QS. Prove that (i) PQ = PS, (ii) PR bisects $\angle$ QRS, (iii) PS is a tangent to the circle passing through R, S, X.

14. Two circles touch at P; lines APB and CPD meet one circle at A and C and the other at B and D. Prove that AC is parallel to BD.

If the angle between the tangents at A and P to one circle is equal to the angle between the tangents at P and D to the other circle, prove that AB = CD.

15. The tangent at C to the circumcircle of acute-angled $\triangle$ ABC meets AB produced at D. Circle CBD meets AC produced at E. By producing DC to F, prove that DC = DE and that DE is a tangent to the circle ABE.

CIRCLE CONSTRUCTIONS

Circles from simple data; inscribed and circumscribed circles of a triangle; the tangent at a point; a tangent from an external point; a segment containing a given angle.

EXERCISE 46

1. Draw two triangles having sides of 8 cm, 7 cm and 6 cm. Construct the circumcircle of one and the incircle of the other. Measure their radii.

2. The radius of the circumcircle of a triangle is 5 cm and the angles of the triangle are 50°, 60°, 70°. Construct the triangle and measure its sides.

3. The angles of a triangle are 50°, 60°, 70° and the radius of the incircle is 2 cm. Construct the triangle and measure its sides.

4. (i) On a line 6 cm long draw a segment of a circle containing an angle of 65°. Measure the radius.

(ii) On a line 6 cm long draw a segment of a circle containing an angle of 105°. Measure the radius.

5. Draw a circle of radius 3 cm and a chord of length 5 cm. Construct the tangents at the ends of the chord and measure the angle between them.

6. Draw a circle of radius $4\frac{1}{2}$ cm. Mark a point 10 cm from the centre and construct the tangents from it. Measure their lengths.

7. Draw $\triangle$ ABC having AB = 6 cm, BC = 7 cm, CA = 4.5 cm. Construct two concentric circles so that one passes through A and B and the other touches AC at C. Measure their radii.

8. Construct $\triangle$ PQR so that QR = 8 cm, $\angle$ P = 70° and median PM = 5 cm.

9. On a line PQ of length 9.2 cm draw a semicircle and construct two circles of radii 2 cm touching the semicircle and PQ. Measure the distance between the centres of the circles.

10. Draw two circles of radii 3 cm and 2 cm touching each other externally. Draw an arc of radius 7 cm to touch the two circles.

INTERSECTING CHORDS

1. Two chords AB, CD intersect at X.
    (i) If AX = 7, XB = 3, CX = 5, calculate XD.
    (ii) If AX = 3.2, XB = 3.6, CX = 2XD, calculate CD.

2. Chords PQ, RS are produced to meet at X and XT is a tangent.

    (i) If PQ = 6, QX = 4, XS = 5, calculate RS.
    (ii) If PQ = 9, QX = 3, calculate XT.
    (iii) If PQ = 3, QX = 5, RS = 6, calculate SX.
    (iv) If XS = x, SR = $x + 1$, XT = $x + 2$, calculate x.

3. Chord CD cuts diameter AB at right angles at P. If AB = 13, CD = 12 and O is the centre of the circle, find OP.

4. Two circles cut at A and B. A line CEXDF meets AB at X, one circle at C and D and the other at E and F. If CE = 9, EX = 3, XD = 2, AX = 4, calculate XB and DF.

5. An arch of a bridge has the form of an arc of a circle. If the width of the arch is 16 m and the greatest height is 3 m, calculate the radius.

If the width is $2y$ m, the greatest height is x m and the radius is r m, express r in terms of x and y.

6. Diameter AB is produced to C and CE is a tangent. If AB = $2r$, BC = h, CE = d, prove that $h^2 + 2rh - d^2 = 0$. If h is very small compared with r, show that approximately $d^2 = 2rh$.

Taking the radius of the Earth as 6.37×10^3 km, show that a man on a cliff of height k m can see a distance d km out to sea where $d = 3\frac{1}{2}\sqrt{k}$ approximately.

7. Two circles intersect at A and B; PQ, PR are the tangents from a point P on AB produced. (One to each circle.) Prove that PQ = PR.

8. Altitudes AD and BE of acute-angled $\triangle$ ABC intersect at H. Complete, giving reasons:

(i) BH . HE = ...; (ii) BH . BE = ...; (iii) CD . CB = ...

9. In quad. ABCD, AB is parallel to DC; a circle through A and B cuts AD and BC at P and Q; PC and QD intersect at O. Prove that PO . OC = QO . OD.

10. A circle passes through the vertices of $\triangle$ ABC; a line parallel to the tangent at A meets AB, AC at D, E. Prove that AD . AB = AE . AC. Is the result true if D, E are on BA produced, CA produced?

11. Two circles intersect at A and B; AB is produced to C and a circle, centre C, passing through A, cuts the first two circles at D and E; CD and CE cut the circles at F and G. Prove that DF = GE.

12. Two circles intersect at A and B; P is a point on AB; CPD is a chord of one circle and EPF is a chord of the other. Prove that C, E, D, F are concyclic.

13. AB is a diameter of a circle; chords AC and AD are produced to meet the tangent at B at E and F. Prove that (i) AB is a tangent to the circle BCE, (ii) AB^2 = AC . AE, (ii) C, E, F, D are concyclic.

PROPORTIONAL INTERCEPTS AND
SIMILAR TRIANGLES

EXERCISE 48

1. [Fig. 13.] Find x, y, v, w.

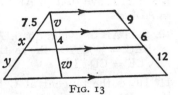

FIG. 13

2. In $\triangle$ ABC, AB $= 4$ cm, AC $= 3$ cm, $\angle$ A $= 90°$; D is a point on AB such that $\angle$ ACD $= \angle$ ABC. Calculate (i) BC, (ii) CD, (iii) AD.

3. D, E, F are points on sides BC, CA, AB of $\triangle$ ABC such that DF, FE are parallel to CA, BC; BD $= 7\frac{1}{2}$ cm, DC $= 10$ cm, AE $= 8$ cm, BF $= 9$ cm. Calculate AF and CE.

4. The sides AB, DC of cyclic quad. ABCD are produced to meet at X; the diagonals intersect at Y. Name a triangle similar to each of the following triangles: ABY, CBX, ACX. If CX $=$ CD and BX : CX $= 2 : 3$, calculate BC : AD, AB : BX and AY : YD.

5. Two circles intersect at A and B. The tangent to the first circle at A meets the second at C and the tangent to the second circle at B meets the first at D. If AD $= 15$ cm, AB $= 12$ cm, BD $= 18$ cm, calculate AC and BC.

6. P is a point on side KM of $\triangle$ KLM such that KP : PM $= 3 : 4$; Q is a point on KL such that KQ : QL $= 2 : 5$; QP produced meets LM produced at N; a line through M parallel to PQ meets LK at R. Calculate LM : MN and verify that
$$\frac{LN}{NM} \cdot \frac{MP}{PK} \cdot \frac{KQ}{QL} = 1.$$

7. (i) Draw a line of length 8 cm and divide it internally in the ratio 4 : 5. Measure each part.

(ii) Draw a line of length 6 cm and divide it externally in the ratio 7 : 2. Measure each part.

73

8. △s ABP, ABQ are on opposite sides of AB. R, S, T are points on AB, AP, AQ such that RS is parallel to BP and RT is parallel to BQ. Prove that (i) AS : SP = AT : TQ and (ii) ST is parallel to PQ.

9. D is a point on side AB of △ ABC. A line through D parallel to BC meets AC at E and a line through E parallel to CD meets AB at F. Prove that (i) AF : FD = AD : DB and (ii) AF . AB = AD².

10. Side AB of cyclic quad. ABCD is produced to E so that ∠ BEC = ∠ CAD. Prove that (i) ∠ ACD = ∠ BCE, (ii) AC : CE = CD : BC.

11. DC is the tangent at C to the circumcircle of △ ABC. If ∠ BAC = ∠ CAD, prove that (i) △s ABC, ACD are similar, (ii) AB . AD = AC².

12. ABCD is a rectangle; P is a point on AB such that ∠ CPD = 90°. Prove that (i) the three triangles are similar, (ii) DP² = AP . DC, (iii) CP² : DP² = BP : PA.

13. The diagonals of par. ABCD intersect at O. If ∠ ABD = ∠ CAD, prove that (i) △s AOD, BCD are similar, (ii) AC . BD = 2AD . DC.

14. P is a point on side BC of quad. ABCD; Q, R are points on AC, CD such that PQ, PR are parallel to BA, BD. Prove that QR is parallel to AD. Iĭ S is a point on AB such that PS is parallel to CA, is SR parallel to AD?

RATIO OF AREAS OF SIMILAR TRIANGLES

EXERCISE 49

2. The sides of a triangle are 12 cm, 9 cm, 8 cm. A second triangle is similar to the first and has a side of 6 cm. Calculate the three possible ratios of the areas.

2. In quad. ABCD, AB is parallel to DC and AC and BD intersect at X; AB = 6 cm, CD = 10 cm. Calculate (i) AX : AC, (ii) $\triangle$AXB : $\triangle$ AXD, (iii) $\triangle$ AXB : $\triangle$ CXD.

3. Line PQ is drawn parallel to side BC of $\triangle$ ABC and meets AB, AC at P, Q; PR is drawn parallel to BQ and meets AC at R. If AP : PB = 3 : 2, calculate (i) $\triangle$ APR : $\triangle$ APQ, (ii) $\triangle$ APQ : $\triangle$ ABC, (iii) $\triangle$ APR : $\triangle$ ABC.

4. Chords AB, CD of a circle intersect at Q. If AQ = 6 cm, QB = 4 cm, CQ = 3 cm, calculate (i) CD, (ii) $\triangle$ AQC : $\triangle$ BQD, (iii) $\triangle$ AQD : $\triangle$ BQC, (iv) $\triangle$ ACB : $\triangle$ ADB.

5. P, R are points on side AB of $\triangle$ ABC such that AP = 4 cm, PR = 3 cm, RB = 5 cm; lines through P, R parallel to BC meet AC at Q, S; AQ = 3 cm. Calculate QS and SC. If the area of $\triangle$ ABC is 48 cm², calculate the areas of $\triangle$ APQ, $\triangle$ PCR and quad. BRSC.

6. P, Q are the mid-points of sides AB, CD of par. ABCD; PQ, AC intersect at R; BQ, AC intersect at S. Prove that AS = 2SC and express the areas of CQR, SQC, ADQS as fractions of the area of par. ABCD.

7. Chord AB is produced to P. PT is a tangent. Prove that $\triangle$s ATP, TBP are similar. By expressing the ratio of the areas of these triangles in two ways, prove that $AT^2 : BT^2 = AP : BP$.

8. Altitudes AD, BE of $\triangle$ ABC intersect at H. Prove that (i) $\dfrac{\triangle \text{ DEC}}{\triangle \text{ ABC}} = \dfrac{DC^2}{AC^2}$, (ii) $\dfrac{\triangle \text{ DEC}}{\triangle \text{ ABC}} = \dfrac{\triangle \text{ HED}}{\triangle \text{ AHB}}$.

ANGLE BISECTOR THEOREM

EXERCISE 50

Questions 1 to 3: The interior and exterior bisectors of $\angle$ A of $\triangle$ ABC meet BC at D and BC produced at E.

1. If AB = 10, BC = $10\frac{1}{2}$, AC = 4, calculate BD, BE, $\angle$ DAE and the circumradius of $\triangle$ ADE.

2. If BD = 4.9, DC = 3.5, AB = 7, calculate AC and CE.

3. If BC = 16, AD = 18, AB : AC = 5 : 3, calculate AE, the area of $\triangle$ DAE and the area of $\triangle$ ABC.

4. I is the centre of the circle touching the sides of $\triangle$ ABC and AI produced meets BC at D. If AB = 12, BC = 10, CA = 8, calculate BD and AI : ID.

5. In quad. ABCD, AB = 6, BC = 9, CD = 12, DA = 8. Prove that the bisectors of $\angle$ B and $\angle$ D meet on AC.

6. P is a point NOT on straight line ABCD. If AB = 14, BC = 6, CD = 15, BP = 8, DP = 20, prove that PA and PC bisect $\angle$ BPD.

7. The bisector of $\angle$ A of $\triangle$ ABC meets BC at D; line DE is parallel to BA and meets AC at E. Prove that AE : EC = AB : AC.

8. Chords AB, CD of a circle intersect at X; the bisector of $\angle$ AXC meets AC, BD at E, F. Prove that AE : EC = DF : FB.

9. In quad. PQRS, QR = RS; RL, RM bisect $\angle$ PRQ, $\angle$ PRS and meet PQ, PS at L. M. Prove that LM is parallel to QS.

10. M is the mid-point of side BC of $\triangle$ ABC. The bisector of $\angle$ AMB meets AB at D. A line through D parallel to BC meets AC at E. Prove that ME bisects $\angle$ AMC.

11. Two circles, centres O and P, touch at T. A line ABCD parallel to OP meets one circle at A, B and the other at C, D; AO and DP are produced to meet at S. Prove that ST bisects ∠ OSP.

12. P, Q are points on side BC of △ ABC such that BP = QC; BT bisects ∠ ABC and cuts AP, AQ, AC at R, S, T. Prove that $\dfrac{PR}{AR} + \dfrac{QS}{SA} = \dfrac{CT}{AT}$.

LOCI

EXERCISE 51

1. State the locus of point P in each of the following cases, illustrating by a sketch:

(i) P is 1 cm from a fixed straight line of infinite length.

(ii) P is 2 cm from a fixed point A.

(iii) P is equidistant from two fixed points B and C.

(iv) P is equidistant from two fixed straight lines DE and DF.

(v) G and H are fixed points and the area of △ GPH is constant.

(vi) K and L are fixed points and $KP^2 + LP^2 = KL^2$.

(vii) M and N are fixed points and ∠ MPN is constant.

2. Draw △ ABC having AB = 8 cm, BC = 6 cm, CA = 7 cm. Construct (i) the locus of points equidistant from B and C, and (ii) the locus of points 3 cm from the mid-point of AB. Measure the distance between the points of intersection of the loci.

3. Draw △ PQR having PQ = 6 cm, QR = 4.4 cm, RP = 5.2 cm. Construct (i) the locus of points equidistant from RP and QP, and (ii) the locus of points 2 cm from RQ. Mark two points, X and Y, satisfying both conditions and measure XY.

4. Draw a line AB of length 6 cm. Construct (i) the locus of points equidistant from A and B, (ii) the locus of points, C, such that the area of $\triangle$ ABC is 12 cm², (iii) an isosceles triangle ABD of area 12 cm².

5. PQ is a line of length 8 cm and R is its mid-point. State the locus of the centre of a circle:

   (i) if its radius is 2 cm and it touches PQ;

   (ii) if it touches the line at R and has any radius;

   (iii) if it passes through P and R and has any radius.

Illustrate by sketches.

6. State the locus of the centre of the circle in each of the following cases, illustrating each by a sketch:

   (i) a circle of varying radius, touching a fixed circle, centre O, at a fixed point A.

   (ii) a circle of varying radius touching fixed lines BC and BD.

   (iii) a circle of radius 2 cm touching a fixed circle of radius 8 cm, centre E.

7. (*a*) A is a fixed point on the circumference of a fixed circle, centre O; M is the mid-point of a variable chord AB. State the locus of M.

(*b*) PQ is a chord of length 4.2 cm in a circle of radius 2.9 cm. State the locus of T, the mid-point of PQ.

8. (*a*) AB is a tangent at point B on a circle of radius 5 cm. If AB has a constant length 12 cm, state the locus of A.

(*b*) In the circle of (*a*), chord CD is produced to E and CDE varies so that CE . DE = 39 cm². State the locus of E.

9. CD is a fixed line of length 10 cm and Q moves so that CQ : QD = 7 : 3. Let R, T be points on CD, CD produced such that CR : RD = CT : TD = 7 : 3. Using the angle bisector theorem, state facts about QR and QT. Hence find the locus of Q.

THREE-DIMENSIONAL PROBLEMS:
HEIGHTS AND DISTANCES

EXERCISE 52

1. B is 500 m due east of A; C is due north of A and N. 68° W. from B. From A the angle of elevation of the top of a building at C is 12°. Calculate (i) AC; (ii) the height of the building; (iii) the angle of elevation of the top from B.

2. A mast PT stands at the corner P of a rectangular field PQRS; PQ = 60 m and QR = 45 m. From Q the angle of elevation of T is 12°. Calculate the angle of elevation of T from R and from S.

3. ABCD is a rectangular piece of cardboard; AB = 16 cm and BC = 24 cm; L and M are the mid-points of AD and BC. The cardboard is folded about LM so that ∠ ALD = 70°. Calculate AD and ∠ BLC.

4. In △ ABC, AB = AC = 20 cm; ∠ A = 36°; M is the mid-point of BC. The triangle is held so that BC is in contact with a horizontal table and AM is at 40° to the horizontal. Calculate (i) AM; (ii) the height of A above the table; (iii) the inclination of AB to the horizontal.

5. ABCD is a rectangular desk top; AB = 60 cm, AD = 50 cm; AB is horizontal and the slope of BC is 20°; M is a point on AD such that AM = 20 cm. Calculate (i) the height of M above AB; (ii) the height of C above AB; (iii) the slope of MC.

6. P and Q are points 50 m apart on a river bank. A tree stands on the other bank at R, which is directly opposite P. From P the angle of elevation of the top of the tree is 16° and from Q it is 10°. Calculate (i) the height of the tree; (ii) the width of the river.

THREE-DIMENSIONAL PROBLEMS: SOLIDS

EXERCISE 53

1. Fig. 14 represents a cuboid.
Find, in fraction form, the tangent of the angle between:

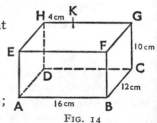

FIG. 14

   (i) AH and the horizontal;
   (ii) AH and the plane ABFE;
   (iii) AG and the plane ABCD;
   (iv) plane AEGC and plane AEFB;
   (v) AG and the plane BCGF.

2. In Fig. 14, calculate the angle between:

   (i) planes ABGH and DCFE;
   (ii) AK and plane ADHE;
   (iii) BK and plane EFGH;
   (iv) AK and KB.

3. Calculate the angle between a diagonal of a cube and (i) an edge; (ii) a face; (iii) another diagonal.

4. V is the vertex of a right pyramid on a rectangular base ABCD. AB = 16 cm, BC = 12 cm, VA = VB = VC = VD = 18 cm. Calculate the angle between:

   (i) AV and the base;   (ii) BV and DV;
   (iii) planes BCV and ABCD;   (iv) planes BCV and ADV;
   (v) planes ABV and DCV.

5. A hemispherical bowl of radius 12 cm is suspended from a point by three chains of length 20 cm attached to points equally spaced on the rim of the bowl. Calculate (i) the inclination of each chain to the horizontal; (ii) the angle between two chains.

6. ABCD is a regular tetrahedron of side 6 cm; N is the foot of the perpendicular from A to base BCD; BN and CN are produced to meet CD and BD at K and L. Calculate: (i) BN; (ii) AK; (iii) AN; (iv) the angle between planes ACD and BCD; (v) the angle between AB and plane BCD.

PLAN AND ELEVATION

EXERCISE 54

Draw plan and elevation views for the following solids:

1. A frustum of a right circular cone, base radius 3 cm, top radius $1\frac{1}{2}$ cm, height 4 cm.

2. The right pyramid of Exercise 53, Question 4.

3. The tetrahedron of Exercise 53, Question 6.

4. A cube, side 4 cm, held with four faces at 45° to the horizontal and two faces vertical.

5. Fig. 15 shows a wedge with three rectangular faces; APRC is in contact with a horizontal table. AB = AC = 9 cm, BC = 5 cm, AP = 7 cm.

Draw (i) the elevation view on a vertical plane parallel to ABC, (ii) the plan view.

Find the inclination of AQ to the horizontal.

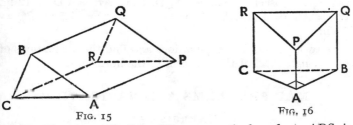

FIG. 15   FIG. 16

6. In Fig. 16, AP, BQ, CR are vertical and △ ABC is horizontal. AP = AB = AC = 60 cm, BQ = CR = 90 cm, ∠ BAC = 90°.

Draw (i) the plan, (ii) the elevation on a plane parallel to BQRC, (iii) the elevation on a plane perpendicular to BQRC.

Find the inclination to the horizontal of (i) PQ, (ii) plane PQR.

7. A post consists of a pyramid TABCD on top of a rectangular prism ABCD, EFGH. ABCD is a square of side 18 cm, AT = BT = CT = DT = 24 cm, AE = BF = CG = DH = 60 cm. Draw (i) a plan, (ii) an elevation perpendicular to the plane ACGE, (iii) an elevation perpendicular to the plane ABFE. State the inclination to the horizontal of (a) AT and (b) face ABT.

8. A sphere, centre P, radius 3 cm, rests on the top ABCD of an open cubical box of side 4 cm.

Draw the elevation views (i) on a vertical plane perpendicular to AB, (ii) on a vertical plane perpendicular to AC.

Find (i) the height of P above the base, (ii) the distance of P from A.

9. Three spheres of radii $2\frac{1}{2}$ cm are placed in contact with each other on a horizontal plane, their centres forming an equilateral triangle ABC. A fourth sphere, centre D, radius $2\frac{1}{2}$ cm, is placed in contact with the other three. Draw (i) the plan, (ii) the elevation on a vertical plane perpendicular to BC.

Find the height of D above the table.

10. A roof consists of two equal trapezia ABPQ, DCPQ and two equal isosceles triangles AQD, BPC. AB = CD = 12 m, BC = AD = 6 m, BP = CP = AQ = DQ = 7.5 m, PQ = 7.5 m.

Draw a plan and two elevations and find the inclinations of the triangles and of the trapezia to the horizontal.

MAP PROBLEMS AND NAVIGATION

EXERCISE 55

1. Find the Representative Fraction for a scale of (i) 1 cm to 1 km, (ii) 25 mm to 1 m.

2. The R.F. of a map is 1 : 63 360. (i) Find, correct to 0.01 km, the actual distance represented by 45 mm. (ii) Find, correct to the nearest millimetre, the distance on the map which represents 10 km.

3. On a map of scale 2 cm to 1 km, the distance along a road between the 400 m and 500 m contours is 1.4 cm. Calculate the average gradient of the road in the form $\dfrac{1}{n}$.

4. The distance between points P and Q on a hillside is 150 m. On a map of scale 10 cm to 1 km PQ is 1.2 cm. If P is on the 200-m contour, find the height of Q.

Questions 5 to 12: Give directions to the nearest degree and speeds to the nearest unit.

Find the magnitude and direction of the resultant of the following pairs of velocities:

5. Equal velocities of 10 m/s, one due north and the other in the direction 240°.

6. 18 km/h in the direction 055° and 6 km/h in the direction 102°.

Find the ground speed and track in the following cases:

7. Air speed 400 km/h, course 280°; wind 80 km/h from 065°.

8. Air speed 640 km/h, course 030°; wind 70 km/h from 145°.

Find the wind velocity:

9. Air speed 375 km/h, course 139°; track 128°, ground speed 366 km/h.

10. Air speed 512 km/h, course 206°; track 218°, ground speed 488 km/h.

Find the drift and ground speed in the following cases:

11. Air speed 400 km/h; track 080°; wind 60 km/h from 150°.

12. Air speed 390 km/h; track 238°; wind 75 km/h from 305°.

13. The bearing of Q from P is 060°. A boat which has a speed of 10 knots in still water sets a course of 050° to travel from P to Q when there is a current from the west. Find the speed of the current and the distance PQ if the boat takes $\frac{1}{2}$ h.

14. A boat is travelling at 10 knots eastwards in a current coming from 050°. If the speed of the boat in still water is 12 knots, find the speed of the current and the course set for the boat.

15. An aircraft having an air speed of 400 km/h is required to fly 320 km on a track of 164°. The wind is blowing at 64 km/h from 280°. Find the course, ground speed and time taken.

16. A navigator flying on a course of 260° at an air speed of 500 km/h makes good a track of 251° at a ground speed of 450 km/h. Find the speed and direction of the wind.

17. A pilot sets a course of 030° and an air speed of 560 km/h. If the wind is blowing at 104 km/h from 110°, find the track and ground speed.

18. A helicopter which has an air speed of 180 km/h is required to travel 150 km due north. There is a wind of 60 km/h, and the pilot has to set a course of 015°. Find (i) the two possible directions of the wind; (ii) the two possible times for the journey.

ARCS, LATITUDE AND LONGITUDE

EXERCISE 56

Arc AB of a circle, radius r, subtends an angle of θ at the centre.

1. If $r = 5$ and $\theta = 48°$, calculate arc AB.

2. If $r = 6$ and arc AB = 8, calculate θ.

3. If $r = 10$ and chord AB = 12, calculate arc AB.

4. If $r = 8$ and arc AB = 18, calculate chord AB.

5. If $r = 6$ and $\theta = 64°$, calculate the area of sector OAB.

6. If $r = 10$ and $\theta = 50°$, calculate the area of minor segment AB.

7. A sector of radius 10 cm and angle 150° is bent to form the curved surface of a cone. Calculate (i) the radius of the cone; (ii) the vertical angle; (iii) the vertical height.

8. The curved surface of a cone of vertical angle 100° is flattened to form a sector of a circle. Calculate, correct to the nearest degree, the angle of the sector.

Take the radius of the Earth as 6371 kilometres. Give answers in kilometres, unless instructed otherwise.

Questions 9 to 14:
P has latitude 50° N. and longitude 10° W.,
Q has latitude 50° N. and longitude 85° W.,
R has latitude 35° S. and longitude 10° W.

9. Calculate the distance between P and R along the meridian.

10. Calculate the radius of the circle of lat. 50° N.

11. Calculate the distance between P and Q along the circle of latitude.

12. Calculate the distance of Q from the equator.

13. Calculate the length of chord PQ, i.e. the straight line through the Earth.

14. Calculate the angle subtended by PQ at the centre of the Earth and hence the Great Circle distance from P to Q.

15. A and B are 7789 km apart along a circle of latitude. Their longitudes are 10° E. and 140° W. Calculate their latitude.

16. Calculate the speed of Edinburgh, lat. 56° N., due to the rotation of the Earth.

17. Calculate the difference in local time between New York, 40° 20′ N., 74° 0′ W., and Bombay, 22° 0′ N., 72° 15′ E.

18. A ship sails 1746 km due north from Auckland, lat. 36° 54′ S. Calculate its new latitude.

19. Calculate the distance between Hong Kong, lat. 22° 20′ N. and Brunei, lat. 4° 55′ N., assuming that they have the same longitude.

20. A ship sails 250 nautical miles along the parallel of latitude 60° N. Calculate its change in longitude. [1 nautical mile = 1.852 km.]

21. A ship sails 200 nautical miles due west and its longitude changes by 5°. Calculate the latitude of the ship.

22. C and D both have a latitude of 55° N. and their longitudes are 95° W. and 35° E. Calculate (i) the radius of the circle of latitude; (ii) the straight line CD; (iii) the angle at the centre of the Earth subtended by CD; (iv) the Great Circle distance CD.

23. Calculate the shorter Great Circle distance between Buenos Aires, 34° S., 58° W., and Sydney, 34° S., 151° E.

TEST PAPERS

PAPER I

1. (i) Calculate $(0.3)^2 \times (0.4)^2 \times 50$.

(ii) Express $\frac{7}{16}$ and $\frac{19}{250}$ as exact decimals.

(iii) When making 1000 revolutions a cycle wheel travels 2.2 kilometres. Find its diameter in centimetres.

2. (i) Factorize: $9a^2 - 4b^2$ and $8x^2 - 4x - 4$.

(ii) If $y = px^2 + q$, express x in terms of y, p and q.

(iii) Solve $3x - 4y = 22$, $5x + 6y = 5$.

3. (i) Without using tables, evaluate $1 - \sin^2 60°$ and $\tan 120°$.

(ii) Find a value of x such that $\sin 4x = \cos 5x$.

(iii) PQ is a chord of a circle, centre O; PQ = 18 cm and OP = 15 cm; M is the mid-point of chord PQ and R is any point on minor arc PQ. Calculate OM, $\angle$ POQ, $\angle$ PRQ and the area of $\triangle$ POQ.

4. The diagonals of square ABCD intersect at P; the bisector of $\angle$ DAC meets PD at Q; the bisector of $\angle$ ABD meets AC, AQ at R, T. Prove that (i) $\angle$ ATB = 90°; (ii) A, T, P, B are concyclic; (iii) T, R, P, Q are concyclic; (iv) BQ = AB; (v) RQ $\parallel$ AD.

5. (i) If £1 = 11.80 francs, convert 400 francs into pounds and pence, correct to the nearest penny.

(ii) An alloy is formed by mixing copper and zinc in the ratio by mass of 13 : 7. Find, correct to the nearest cm³, the volume of a block of mass 1 kg.

[The specific gravity of copper is 8.8 and that of zinc is 7.2.]

6. A, B, C are points on a horizontal plane; A is 80 m SW. of C and B is SE. of C; the bearing of B from A is N. 68° E. From A the angle of elevation of the top T of a tower at C is 36°. Calculate the height of the tower and the angle of elevation of T from B.

PAPER 2

1. (i) Simplify $(4\frac{1}{4} - 3\frac{1}{6}) \div (3\frac{1}{4} + 4\frac{1}{3})$.

(ii) Calculate the simple interest on £480 for 7 months at $4\frac{1}{2}\%$ p.a.

(iii) If $\tan \theta = -\frac{8}{15}$, find, without tables, $\sin \theta$ and $\cos \theta$.

2. (i) Simplify $(p + 5)^2 - (p - 5)^2 - 5p$.

(ii) Express as a single fraction $\dfrac{1 - y}{y} + \dfrac{y}{1 + y}$.

(iii) Solve $\frac{1}{4}(3x - 4) + 2\frac{1}{2} = \frac{3}{5}(x + 4)$.

3. (i) The interior angle of a regular polygon is 144°. How many sides has the polygon? If A, B, C, D, E are consecutive vertices, calculate the angle between AC and BE.

(ii) From a point P outside a circle a tangent PT is drawn to touch the circle at T; a line PAB meets the circle at A and B. If TA = 4 cm, TP = 5 cm, BP = 6 cm, calculate AB and BT.

4. Find the maximum and minimum points on the curve $y = x^3 - 6x^2 + 9x$. Sketch the curve showing these points. Find the area between the curve and the x axis.

5. (i) A cone and a sphere have equal radii and equal volumes. Show that the height of the cone is twice the diameter of the sphere.

(ii) Rain falling on a flat rectangular roof 6.6 m by 4.5 m flows into a cylindrical tank of diameter 1.2 m. Find, in millimetres, the increase in depth of water in the tank caused by 1.2 mm of rain.

6. (i) y is inversely proportional to x^2 and $y = 4\frac{1}{2}$ when $x = 8$. Find y when $x = 6$ and find x when $y = 18$. For what value of x is $y = \frac{1}{6}x$?

(ii) Find the speed of Trinidad, lat. 10° N., due to the rotation of the Earth and the latitude of a place which has half this speed.

PAPER 3

1. (i) Express £2.77½ as a decimal of £18.50.

   (ii) The volume of a sphere is $179\frac{2}{3}$ cm³. Find its radius.

   (iii) Evaluate, correct to 3 sig. fig. $(0.4723)^3$ and $\sqrt[3]{0.2143}$.

2. (i) Evaluate $(64)^{\frac{2}{3}} - (\frac{1}{3})^{-2} - (9^2)^{\frac{1}{2}}$.

   (ii) Solve $5x - 3x^2 = 2$.

   (iii) In $\triangle$ ABC, $a = 7.3$, A $= 72°$, B $= 58\frac{1}{2}°$. Calculate b.

3. (i) In $\triangle$ ABC, AB $= 7$, BC $= 6$; E is a point on AB such that AE $= 4$; EF is parallel to BC and meets AC at F; the bisector of $\angle$ A meets EF, BC at G, H. If AF $= 5$, calculate FC, HC and EG.

   (ii) Squares PQVW and SPXY are drawn outside par. PQRS. Prove by congruency that $\angle$ QPR $= \angle$ PWX and that RP produced is perpendicular to WX.

4. AB is a chord of a circle, centre O, and $\angle$ AOB is less than 120°; PAQ is a tangent such that AB $=$ PB; PB produced meets the circle again at R. (i) Prove that AP $=$ AR and that $\angle$ QAR $= \angle$ ABR. (ii) If AP $= 6$ and PB $= 4.8$ calculate BR and $\angle$ BAR.

5. Find the area between curve $y = 3x^2 + 1$, the x axis and the ordinates $x = 1$ and $x = 3$. Find also the volume formed by rotating this area about the x axis.

6. During one week a shopkeeper sold 100 articles at a profit of $33\frac{1}{3}\%$ of their cost price, which was $37\frac{1}{2}$p each. The next week he sold 120 at a discount of 5% on the previous selling price. Find his actual profit in each of the weeks.

   In the third week he sold the articles at the same price as in the second and his profit was the same as in the first week. How many did he sell?

PAPER 4

1. (i) Evaluate, to 3 sig. fig., $62.3(\sin 21° 43')^2$.

(ii) Calculate, correct to the nearest square metre, the area of the walls of a room 4.6 m long, 3.3 m wide and 2.4 m high.

(iii) By selling an article for £1.80 a trader makes 20% profit on his cost price. At what price should he sell it to make $33\frac{1}{3}$% on his cost price?

2. (i) Factorize $6x^2 + 5xy - 21y^2$ and $xy - 4x + 5y - 20$.

(ii) Differentiate $2x^5 + 4x^2 + \dfrac{6}{x^2}$ and integrate $2x^3 + 3 + \dfrac{4}{x^2}$.

(iii) If $N = 188\sqrt{\dfrac{EI}{wl^4}}$, express l in terms of E, I, N and w. Calculate l if $w = 0.24$, $E = 30 \times 10^6$, $I = 0.0347$, $N = 4900$.

3. (i) ABCD is a quadrilateral. A, B, C are fixed. State the locus of D if (a) AD = CD, (b) $\angle$ A + $\angle$ C = 180°, (c) the area of quad. ABCD is constant.

(ii) In par. PQRS, PQ = 4 cm, QR = 7 cm, $\angle$ PQR = 74°. Calculate PR and the area of PQRS.

4. In rectangle ABCD, AB = 9 cm, AD = 7 cm; P, Q are points on AB, AD and AP = AQ = x cm. Find an expression for the area of $\triangle$ PQC. Find, correct to 2 dec. pl., the value of x for $\triangle$ PQC to have one-third the area of the rectangle.

5. The sides AB, DC of quad. ABCD are produced to meet at P; the sides AD, BC are produced to meet at Q. Prove (i) that if CP = 2DC and CQ = 2 BC then BD is parallel to PQ and AQ : AD = AP : AB, but (ii) that if CP = 2BC and CQ = 2DC, then B, P, Q, D are concyclic and AQ . AD = AP . AB.

6. An aircraft has a course of 295° and an air speed of 420 km/h. The wind is blowing at 80 km/h from the south.

(i) Find the ground speed and track of the aircraft.

(ii) If the aircraft is to fly to a point in the direction 225°, what course should be set?

PAPER 5

1. (i) A man covers 10 m when he makes 12 paces. If he makes 112 paces per minute what is his speed in km/h?

   (ii) Christmas cards are bought at £2.50 per 100 and sold at $42\frac{1}{2}$p per dozen. Find the profit per cent on outlay.

   (iii) Find the area of a triangle having sides of 8, 11, 13 cm.

2. (i) If $s = ut + \frac{1}{2}ft^2$, express f in terms of s, u and t.

   (ii) Simplify $\dfrac{x}{x^2 - 2x - 3} - \dfrac{2}{x^2 - x - 6}$.

   (iii) Solve $5x^2 = 4x + 7$, correct to 2 dec. pl.

3. (i) In cyclic quad. ABCD, $\angle$ BAD = 104°, $\angle$ ACD = 48°; the tangent at A is parallel to DC. Calculate $\angle$ ADB, $\angle$ BAC and $\angle$ ABC.

   (ii) Side SR of par. PQRS is produced to T. Prove that $\triangle$ PRT = $\triangle$ QRT and that $\triangle$ PST = quad. PQTR.

4. The base of a pyramid is a square ABCD of side 8 cm. Edges VA and VB are each 10 cm and face VAB is inclined at 50° to the base. Calculate (i) the height of V above the base; (ii) the angle between VCD and the base; (iii) the length of VC.

5. After a motorway has been opened a motorist finds that his time for a journey of 154 km is reduced by 1 h 10 min. If his average speed has increased by 22 km/h, find his former average speed.

6. A particle starts from rest and moves in a straight line so that its acceleration at time t s is $(3 - \frac{1}{4}t)$ m/s^2.

   (i) Find its maximum speed in the positive direction.

   (ii) When is the particle again at rest and how far is it from its starting point?

   (iii) At what time and with what speed does it pass through the starting point?

   (iv) When is its speed 16 m/s?

ANSWERS

1. £28.12

2. £4.64

3. 35

4. 180 francs

5. £3440.59

6. £52.84

7. 22.680 kg

8. 64 mm

9. 11, 27p

10. 13 620

11. £53.04

12. 205

13. £23.40

14. £1996.40

15. £5.50

16. £15.53

EXERCISE 2 (page 5)

1. $3\frac{1}{8}$

2. $\frac{1}{2}$

3. $3\frac{1}{3}$

4. 2

5. $5\frac{1}{3}$

6. $\frac{3}{10}$

7. $\frac{15}{16}$

8. $1\frac{1}{4}$

9. $\frac{2}{3}$

10. $10\frac{2}{5}$

11. 12

12. $2\frac{1}{10}$

13. $2\frac{2}{5}$

14. $\frac{4}{5}$

15. $2\frac{7}{13}$

16. $1\frac{3}{8}$

17. $\frac{2}{15}$

18. 6

19. $12\frac{1}{4}$, $1\frac{32}{49}$, $7\frac{9}{16}$; $1\frac{1}{4}$, $2\frac{1}{2}$, $1\frac{3}{5}$

20. $3\frac{3}{8}$, $12\frac{19}{27}$; $1\frac{1}{3}$, $1\frac{3}{4}$

21. $\frac{1}{12}$

22. $\frac{5}{9}$, $\frac{11}{18}$, $\frac{7}{12}$; $1\frac{1}{10}$

23. $\frac{3}{160}$

24. $\frac{7}{16}$

25. $\frac{1}{12}$

26. $\frac{2}{9}$

27. $\frac{3}{4}$

EXERCISE 3 (page 6)

1. 18.2

2. 0.5612

3. 0.327

4. 27.8

5. 0.0359

6. 0.0384

7. 0.178

8. 870

9. 0.003

10. 50

11. 0.4

12. 0.18

13. 0.4375, 0.076

14. 0.09375, 0.0448

15. 0.6667, 0.4545, 0.04286

16. 0.6923, 0.9474, 0.0447

17. 0.32　　**18.** 46 min 48 s　**19.** 0.053　　**20.** 0.76

21. 52370　　**22.** 0.4743　　**23.** 0.0661　　**24.** 121

Exercise 4 (page 7)

1. 35.3 dol　　**2.** 2.15 kg　　**3.** 37p　　　**4.** 18 kg

5. 33 km/h　　**6.** 15 m/s, 250 m/s　　　**7.** 138

8. 25　　　　**9.** 8　　　**10.** 70 km/h　**11.** 16 yr 8 mon

Exercise 5 (page 8)

1. £279　　　　　**2.** 3 : 20　　　　**3.** 38p, £17.10

4. 75 ; 64　　　　**5.** £2.80　　　　**6.** 84 days

7. 1875 litres　　**8.** 360　　　　　**9.** 20

10. 0.68 g　　　　**11.** 54　　　　　**12.** 480 m ; 14.4 ha

13. 13 : 27　　　　**14.** £5.37　　　　**15.** £181.50

16. £3 166 080, £8.73

17. 5 h, 80 h, 10 h ; 1900 km, 1520 km, 570 km

Exercise 6 (page 9)

1. $34\frac{1}{2}$ p ; 56% ; £7　**2.** 34% ; 25 ; 293　　**3.** £6.25

4. £88.75　　　　**5.** 25%　　　　　**6.** 7p

7. £5.20　　　　　**8.** £27

9. $x\left(1 + \dfrac{y}{100}\right)$ fr ; $\dfrac{100z}{100 + y}$ fr　　**10.** 7 dol 80 c

11. £98　　　**12.** £17.10 ; 14%　　**13.** 26.85 fr per m

14. £630, £960, £648　**15.** 15%

EXERCISE 7 (page 11)

1. £112, £752 **2.** 2½, £137.50 **3.** 5, £167.40

4. £46.80, £213.20 **5.** 7, £43.40 **6.** £368, £443.90

7. £190, £114 **8.** £51.87, £298.87 **9.** £318, £21.20

10. £890, £120.15 **11.** £16.19 **12.** £164

13. £41 **14.** £10.32 **15.** £15.61

16. £46.30 **17.** £405, £500 **18.** 3⅓%

19. £128.12 **20.** £1.4%

EXERCISE 8 (page 12)

1. 2.182, 6.899, 21.82, 0.06899, 0.2182

2. 9.668, 51.23, 3.975, 125.7, 0.3975

3. 0.6573, 0.2078, 26.79, 0.8471, 7.595

4. 4529, 316 100, 0.5822, 0.005822, 0.05683

5. 0.1171, 0.01171, 3.073, 42.32, 0.002362

6. 0.5346, 0.4714, 1.803, 2.374

7. 424.9 **8.** 3.526 **9.** 13.42 **10.** 18.88

11. 60.87 **12.** 775.0 **13.** 12.88 **14.** 2.111

15. 0.6369 **16.** 6.403 **17.** 19.79 **18.** 0.7968

19. 0.3596 **20.** 0.3922 **21.** 0.007191 **22.** 0.05710

23. 0.09605 **24.** 0.60206, 0.90309, 0.69897

25. 0.130 **26.** 0.246 **27.** 0.111 **28.** 32.6

29. 639 **30.** 0.362 **31.** 6.70 **32.** 14.4

33. 0.230 **34.** 58.4 **35.** 22.1 **36.** 0.0794

37. 1.81 **38.** 0.905 **39.** 2.52 **40.** 1.75

41. 3.09 **42.** 0.240 **43.** 3080 **44.** 1.53

EXERCISE 9 (page 14)

1. 1.66 km, 16.8 ha   **2.** 3.5 m   **3.** £1.64

4. 108 cm², 6.75 cm   **5.** 90 cm²   **6.** 96 cm³; 6 cm

7. £3.85   **8.** 3360 l, 85 cm   **9.** 1456 cm³

10. 96 cm³   **11.** 1800 t   **12.** 440 cm³

EXERCISE 10 (page 15)

1. 19.8 m   **2.** 42 cm   **3.** 346.5 cm²

4. 22 cm   **5.** $240\frac{5}{8}$ cm²   **6.** 880 cm³

7. 171.6 cm²   **8.** 28 cm   **9.** 231 cm³, 209 cm²

10. 1188 g   **11.** $5\frac{1}{4}$ cm, $346\frac{1}{2}$ cm²   **12.** 6.6 cm³

13. $282\frac{6}{7}$ cm²   **14.** $716\frac{4}{7}$ cm³   **15.** $40\frac{3}{4}$ cm³

16. 16.5 cm   **17.** 389   **18.** 2602 l

19. 3.67 kg   **20.** 4.63 cm   **21.** 95.8(5) g, 1.34 cm

EXERCISE 11 (page 17)

1. $a + b + 4c$ **2.** $x^2 + y^2 + z^2$ **3.** $9p^2 - 16pq - 7q^2$

4. $3x^2 - 4$ **5.** $-2a^2b^2$ **6.** $2a^2$

7. $7ef - 11f^2$ **8.** $33 - 11g$ **9.** $2\frac{3}{5}x$

10. $x^2 + \frac{2}{3}x - \frac{1}{3}$ **11.** $23 - 5h^2$

12. $4y^3 - 11y^2 - 11y - 2$ **13.** $2p^3 - p^2q - 5pq^2 + 3q^3$

14. $15 - 32x + 25x^2 - 12x^3$ **15.** $-7, -8$ **16.** 5, 1

17. $-6y$ **18.** $4fg$ **20.** $2a^2 + 2ab$ **21.** $4xy + 8y^2$

22. $25(x^2 - y^2)$, $25xy$

EXERCISE 12 (page 18)

1. $3a^2(b + 2c)$ **2.** $5d(3d - 5e)$ **3.** $\pi r(r + 2h)$

4. $(a + 2b)(a - 2b)$ **5.** $c(c + 3)(c - 3)$

6. $(5d + 9e)(5d - 9e)$ **7.** $2(3f^2 + 2)(3f^2 - 2)$

8. $2g(2g + 5h)(2g - 5h)$ **9.** $(m^2 + 4)(m + 2)(m - 2)$

10. $3(1 + n^2)(1 + n)(1 - n)$ **11.** $(p - 5)^2$ **12.** $(3r + 2t)^2$

13. $3(2u - 1)^2$ **14.** $(x + 3)^2(x - 3)^2$

15. $(y - 3 + 4z)(y - 3 - 4z)$ **16.** $3(2a + 3)$

17. $(3b - 2)(b + 2)$ **18.** $\pi(a + b)(a - b)$

19. 49   **20.** $2\frac{1}{4}$ **21.** 9   **22.** $9y^2$

23. $6\frac{1}{4}$ **24.** $2\frac{1}{4}x^2$ **25.** $\frac{1}{36}$, $x + \frac{1}{6}$

26. $\frac{9}{25}$, $x - \frac{3}{5}$ **27.** $14\,960$; 1508 **28.** 3600; 1400

29. 450; 128 **30.** 330

31. $(a - c)(b + d)$ **32.** $(f + 2g)(h + 5j)$

33. $(m + p)(m - 3r)$ **34.** $(x - y)(y - 4)$

35. $(a + 5)(b - 3)$ **36.** $(3x - y)(1 - 2y)$

37. $(cd + 1)(d - c)$ **38.** $(3 + 7f^2)(1 - 2g)$

39. $(3a - 2b)(p - 3t)$ **40.** $(ab + 5)(ab - 2c)$

41. $(x + y)(1 + x - y)$ **42.** $(p - q)(p + q - 5)$

43. $(a + 3)(a - 3)(b^2 + 2)$ **44.** $(1 - 2x)(1 + 2y)(1 - 2y)$

45. $2(f + 2)(g - 5)$ **46.** $p(4 - p)(3 + q)$

47. $(x + 2)(x - 2)(y + 1)(y - 1)$

48. $2(1 + a)(1 - a)(1 + 2b^2)$

49. $(a + b)(x - y + z)$ **50.** $(3 - c)(2 - d + f)$

51. $(a + 3)(a + 2)$ **52.** $(b - 1)(b - 8)$ **53.** $(c + 4)(c - 2)$

54. $(d - 9)(d + 2)$ **55.** $(1 + 2e)(1 - e)$ **56.** $(1 + 6f)(1 + f)$

57. $(5g + 1)(2g - 1)$ **58.** $h(h + 3)(h - 1)$

59. $2(j + 2)(j - 3)$

60. $3k(1 - 3k)(1 - 5k)$ **61.** $(l^2 - 21)(l^2 + 1)$

62. $(m + 12n)(m + 2n)$ **63.** $(3a + 2)(a + 1)$

64. $(5b - 1)(b - 3)$ **65.** $(2c - 3)(3c + 5)$

66. $(2d - 5)(d + 2)$ **67.** $(4e - 3)(e + 2)$

68. $(4f + 1)(7f - 8)$ **69.** $(3g + 7)(2g + 3)$

70. $(5h - 2j)(h - 2j)$ **71.** $(4k + 3l)(k - 3l)$

72. $(5 + 2m)(2 - 3m)$ **73.** $5(4n + 5)(n - 3)$

74. $3(2 + p^2)(3 + 2p)(3 - 2p)$ **75.** $x(2y + 1)(y - 3)$

76. $q(7p + 2q)(p - 2q)$ **77.** $(x - 1)(x - 9)$

78. $y(y - 8)$ **79.** $2x + 5$

80. $r - 8s$ **81.** 2   **82.** -21

83. 6   **84.** 6   **85.** $(4x + 7)(x + 3)$; $11 \times 37 \times 103$

86. $(3x + 1)(2x + 3)$; 31×23 **87.** $(3a - b)(2a + 3b)$

88. $(4x + y)(x - 2y)$

Exercise 13 (page 20)

1. 5   **2.** $-1\frac{2}{5}$ **3.** 2   **4.** $\frac{1}{5}$

5. $4\frac{1}{2}$ **6.** $-2\frac{5}{7}$ **7.** 9   **8.** $-1\cdot2$

9. $2\frac{2}{11}$ **10.** $\frac{3}{10}$ **11.** 5   **12.** $-2\frac{1}{2}$

13. $0\cdot6$ **14.** 3   **15.** 5   **16.** 30, 32, 34

17. 5   **18.** 6   **19.** 56 and 72 km/h

20. 3 m   **21.** 173

Exercise 14 (page 21)

1. 3, -2 **2.** $\frac{7}{11}$, $\frac{3}{11}$ **3.** $-1, 2$ **4.** $1\frac{3}{11}$, $-\frac{10}{11}$

5. 6, 5   **6.** 3, -5 **7.** 3, -4 **8.** $4\frac{1}{2}$, 3

9. $2\frac{1}{2}$, $1\frac{1}{6}$ **10.** $-3, -2$ **11.** 1.8, 1.5   **12.** $\frac{1}{2}$, $-1\frac{1}{2}$

13. $\frac{1}{2}(a + b)$, $\frac{1}{2}(a - b)$ **14.** $a + 2b, 2a - b$

15. 5   **16.** 4, -5 **17.** -5 **18.** 13, 17

19. 70, 40   **20.** 11.3 g, 13.5 g

21. 23p   **22.** $\frac{13}{18}$

EXERCISE 15 (page 22)

1. 3, 4   **2.** 5, −2   **3.** −3, $\frac{1}{2}$ **4.** 0, −$2\frac{1}{2}$

5. $1\frac{1}{3}$, −$1\frac{1}{2}$ **6.** $\frac{1}{3}$, $\frac{5}{6}$ **7.** $1\frac{1}{3}$ **8.** ±6

9. $2\frac{1}{2}$, $\frac{1}{6}$ **10.** $2\frac{1}{2}$, −$1\frac{1}{2}$ **11.** $\frac{1}{4}$, −3   **12.** 0, −7

13. −7, $3\frac{1}{2}$ **14.** 1, $\frac{1}{3}$ **15.** 1, −$\frac{8}{9}$ **16.** −$\frac{3}{4}$, $1\frac{2}{3}$

17. $x^2 - 2x - 15 = 0$ **18.** $12x^2 - 13x + 3 = 0$

19. $10x^2 + 13x - 30 = 0$ **20.** $2x^2 + 7x = 0$

21. 5; −3   **22.** −15; −$\frac{3}{4}$ **23.** 7·47, −1·47

24. 1.22, −8.22   **25.** 1.21, −3.71   **26.** −3.13(5), −0.53

27. 1.82, 0.18   **28.** 1.93, −0.73   **29.** 13.78, 0.22

30. 2.35, −0.85   **31.** 4.55, −0.55   **32.** −1.63, −0.37

33. 5; 120 cm²   **34.** 39, 80, 89   **35.** 6

36. 9 cm²   **37.** 5 yr   **38.** 10 cm

EXERCISE 16 (page 24)

1. $\frac{3a}{c}$; −$\frac{d}{e}$; $\frac{7f^4}{3}$; −$\frac{4g}{3h}$ **2.** $\frac{3k}{5m}$; −$\frac{n^2}{2p}$; $\frac{3}{s}$; −$2t^4v$

3. 1; −1; None; −1   **4.** $\frac{1}{3}$ **5.** $c - d$

6. $\frac{f - g}{fg}$ **7.** $\frac{5}{h + 1}$ **8.** $\frac{k + 1}{k}$ **9.** $\frac{2(3m - 5)}{3m + 5}$

10. $\frac{n - 2p}{2n}$ **11.** $\frac{rt}{y}$ **12.** $\frac{3x - 1}{x^2}$

13. $3ab, ab, -9a, 3a(b + 1)$

14. $cd^2, -10, cd(d - c), 5c - 5d$

15. $-2, 3f(f - 3), 2(f + 3), 2(f - 3)$

16. $\frac{5a}{4}$ **17.** $\frac{9}{20b}$ **18.** $\frac{3de + 2ce - 5cd}{cde}$

19. $\frac{2h - 5f - 3g}{6fgh}$ **20.** $\frac{11k + 16}{12}$ **21.** $\frac{pm + 4m - 9p}{6pm}$

22. $\dfrac{4}{x(x + 2)}$ **23.** $\dfrac{8(y - 2)}{(y + 3)(y - 5)}$ **24.** $\dfrac{2a}{(3a - 2b)(2a - b)}$

25. $\dfrac{14c}{3c - 6}$ **26.** $5d - 10$ **27.** $\dfrac{2}{(1 + 3f)(1 + f)}$

28. $\dfrac{4gh}{g^2 - h^2}$ **29.** $\dfrac{6m}{(k - m)(k + 3m)}$ **30.** $\dfrac{1}{n(n + 1)}$

31. $\dfrac{7p - 6}{p^2 - 9}$ **32.** $\dfrac{-v}{q^2 + qv}$ **33.** $\dfrac{2}{(x + 1)(x + 3)}$

34. $\dfrac{a^2}{bc}$ **35.** $2d^2$ **36.** $\dfrac{a + 2}{a + 3}$

37. $\dfrac{3b(b - 2)}{2(b + 2)}$ **38.** $\dfrac{7d - 3c}{4c}$ **39.** $\dfrac{x^2 + y^2}{xy}$

40. $\dfrac{p^2 - 3}{3p}$

EXERCISE 17 (page 25)

1. $7\frac{1}{2}$ **2.** 7 **3.** $2\frac{2}{11}$ **4.** $3\frac{1}{2}$

5. -6 **6.** 6 **7.** $\frac{1}{6}$ **8.** $2, -1\frac{1}{2}$

9. $-7\frac{1}{2}$ **10.** $\frac{2}{5}$ **11.** ± 6 **12.** $\frac{2}{3}$

13. $4, -1$ **14.** $\frac{1}{5}, -5$ **15.** $4, \frac{1}{2}$ **16.** $\frac{1}{3}$

17. 1.5 km **18.** 24 **19.** £2.12$\frac{1}{2}$

20. 50 km/h, 60 km/h **21.** 90

EXERCISE 18 (page 27)

1. $100 - xk - ym$ pence **2.** $2(xy + xz + yz)$ m²

3. $\frac{50}{3}xt$ **4.** $\dfrac{18l}{5y}$

5. $\left(\dfrac{n}{x} + \dfrac{n}{y}\right)$ hours **6.** $£(2n - y)\dfrac{x}{100}$

7. $\dfrac{100x}{x+y}$, $\dfrac{100y}{x+y}$ pence

8. $xy\left(1 + \dfrac{z}{100}\right)$ pence

9. $4xy = (x+y)^2 - (x-y)^2$

10. $2w(p+q+2w)$ m²

11. $pqx^2/100$ ares

12. $£xp/100k$

13. $\dfrac{mx+ny}{x+y}$

14. $\dfrac{t_1x_1 + t_2x_2}{t_1 + t_2}$ km/h

15. $\dfrac{(x_1+x_2)v_1\,v_2}{x_1v_2 + x_2v_1}$ km/h

17. $z = x - y(1 + \frac{3}{8}n)$; 128

18. $(5\frac{1}{2}m - 30h)°$; $2.43\frac{7}{11}$

EXERCISE 19 (page 28)

1. 90   **2.** -3 **3.** 144   **4.** $\frac{10}{13}$

5. 0.75   **6.** 11   **7.** $1\frac{1}{9}$ **8.** $3\frac{1}{2}$

9. 3   **10.** 100   **11.** 16.2   **12.** 0.403

EXERCISE 20 (page 29)

1. $\dfrac{c}{2\pi}$ **2.** $\sqrt{\dfrac{A}{\pi}}$ **3.** $x \tan \theta$ **4.** $\dfrac{x}{\cos \theta}$

5. $\dfrac{a}{n^2}$ **6.** $\dfrac{1}{y-c}$ **7.** $\dfrac{v-u}{a}$ **8.** $\sqrt{v^2 - 2fs}$

9. $\dfrac{uT}{\lambda} + a$ **10.** $\dfrac{3-2x}{8+3x}$ **11.** $\dfrac{pa-b}{p-a}$ **12.** $\dfrac{\sqrt{c-b}}{a}$

13. $\sqrt{\left(\dfrac{p^2}{n^2} - k^2\right)}$ **14.** $\dfrac{PQ}{T^2} - R$ **15.** $\sqrt{\left(\dfrac{1-\cos\theta}{1+\cos\theta}\right)}$

16. $\dfrac{t(p-q)}{q}$ **17.** $\dfrac{2(s-ut)}{t^2}$; $1\frac{1}{2}$ **18.** $\sqrt{(a^2 - 2ab)}$; 4

19. $\dfrac{100}{R}\left(\dfrac{A}{P} - 1\right)$; 3 **20.** $\dfrac{S}{2\pi r} - r$; 4 **21.** $\dfrac{uf}{u + f}$; $8\frac{8}{9}$

22. $\dfrac{2c + 1}{c + 1}$ **23.** $2\frac{1}{2}b$; 4 **24.** $\dfrac{r}{p}$

25. $\dfrac{kp^2}{4(k + 1)^2}$ cm^2 **26.** $\dfrac{100(y - x)}{x + y}$

EXERCISE 21 (page 31)

1. 2, $\frac{1}{9}$, 1, 27, $\frac{4}{5}$ **2.** 9, $\frac{1}{4}$, $6\frac{1}{4}$, $\frac{1}{3}$, $\frac{1}{16}$ **3.** 8, $\frac{1}{5}$, $1\frac{1}{3}$, 1, 8

4. $\frac{1}{7}$, 25, 8, 6, $\frac{2}{5}$ **5.** $4\frac{3}{4}$ **6.** 21

7. 16 **8.** $\frac{8}{9}$ **9.** 25

10. 2^2 **11.** 3^4 **12.** 7, -3

13. $\frac{4}{3}$, $-\frac{2}{3}$ **14.** $\frac{5}{3}$, $-\frac{4}{3}$ **15.** a^3. b^{12}, $c^{\frac{1}{9}}$, d^3

16. e^3, $f^{\frac{5}{6}}$, $\dfrac{h}{g}$, k^3 **17.** $2^{\frac{3}{2}}$. 3^{-2}, a^5b^5, $\frac{1}{2}p^{-3}$, $3q^8$

18. $x^{\frac{2}{3}} + 5x^{\frac{1}{3}} - 2$ **19.** $yz^{-\frac{2}{3}}$, $\frac{1}{2}x^2$

20. $x - 2 + x^{-1}$, $x^{\frac{4}{3}} - x^{-\frac{4}{3}}$

EXERCISE 22 (page 32)

1. 5.15 p.m.; 2.13 p.m., 43 km. **2.** 3.45 p.m.

3. 11.38 p.m.; 5.38 km/h; 11.55 p.m.

4. 0.75 cm, 5.25 cm; 2.2 cm, $h = 0.3t + 2.2$

5. 2895, 1156; After 9 yr.

EXERCISE 23 (page 33)

1. $y \propto x^2$, $y = cx^2$; $s \propto \dfrac{1}{t}$, $s = \dfrac{c}{t}$; $T \propto \sqrt{l}$, $T = c\sqrt{l}$;

$h \propto \dfrac{1}{r^3}$, $h = \dfrac{c}{r^3}$

2. $\sqrt{y}$, $\dfrac{1}{t}$, r^2 **4.** $4 \times \frac{5}{3}$, $4 \times \frac{25}{9}$, $4 \times \frac{3}{5}$, $4 \times \sqrt{\frac{3}{5}}$

5. $\frac{9}{16}$, $2\frac{2}{3}$ **6.** 6, 2   **7.** 18, $3\frac{5}{9}$ **8.** $2\frac{2}{3}$, $1\frac{1}{5}$, 6

9. 4   **10.** 80% increase   **11.** $3\frac{1}{3}$; $w = \frac{5}{18}r^2h$

12. $3\frac{1}{2}$; 120   **13.** 60 cm; 480 cm³; $pv = 24\,000$

14. 11; 8 or 15   **15.** $105 + 7\frac{1}{2}x$; £375

EXERCISE 24 (page 35)

3. $-\frac{1}{2}$, $\frac{1}{5}$, $-\frac{3}{2}$, 4, $\frac{5}{8}$ **4.** $y = -\frac{4}{3}x + 9$; $y = -\frac{4}{3}x - 16$

5. 5; $-0.41 < x < 2.41$; 3.24, -1.24; 3.65, -1.65

6. 0.5; $1.5 < x < 4$; 2, 3.5

7. 4.64; 5.85; 3.62; $x^3 + 20x - 120 = 0$

8. $y = \frac{3}{4}x + 1$; $x^2 - 5x + 3 = 0$; 4.30, 0.70

9. 900 cm²; 40 cm by 20 cm

10. 9.48; 0; 3.71, 1.19, -0.90; 5; 1.11, 3.64, -0.74;
$2x^3 - 8x^2 + x + 6 = 0$; $2y = 8 - x$

11. 1.58; $x < 0.72$, 1.25

12. $(-2.06, -2.47)$; $x^2 + 20x + 37 = 0$

13. 2.77; 4.80

EXERCISE 25 (page 37)

1. $3x^2$, $10x$, 7, $-\dfrac{5}{x^2}$, $-\dfrac{12}{x^3}$, 1

2. $12x^2 - 2$ **3.** $6x + \dfrac{10}{x^3}$ **4.** $2x + 1$

5. $-6 + 2x$ **6.** $5 - 4t - 3t^2$ **7.** $-\frac{1}{2} + x^2$

8. $-\dfrac{4}{x^2} - 3 + 2x$ **9.** -4 **10.** 7

11. $-\frac{2}{3}$ **12.** -14 **13.** $1\frac{3}{4}$

14. 5   **15.** 4; $(-1, -1)$ **16.** $(\frac{1}{3}, \frac{1}{3})$

17. $-1\frac{1}{2}$, $-\frac{2}{3}$ **18.** $(3, 6\frac{1}{2})$ **19.** 3; $(1\frac{1}{2}, -4\frac{1}{2})$

20. -1; $(2, 6)$

Exercise 26 (page 38)

1. 25   **2.** 7   **3.** $4\frac{2}{3}$ **4.** 4, -4

5. 21, -11 **6.** $1\frac{1}{4}$, 8   **7.** $(-1, 15)$, $(3, -17)$

8. 36 cm²   **9.** 72   **10.** $V = 900x - 120x^2 + 4x^3$; 5

11. $(24 - 4x)$ cm; 4   **12.** $A = 7x^2 - 40x + 100$; $2\frac{6}{7}$

13. $2 + \dfrac{4}{k}$, $4 + 2k$, $2k + 8 + \dfrac{8}{k}$; 16

Exercise 27 (page 40)

1. $\frac{1}{3}x^3 + c$, $6x^2 + c$, $-\dfrac{1}{x} + c$, $-\dfrac{3}{x^2} + c$

2. $x + \frac{1}{2}x^2 + \frac{1}{3}x^3 + c$

3. $3x^2 - 8x + c$ **4.** $c - \dfrac{6}{x} - 2x^3$ **5.** $c + \frac{1}{3}x^2 - \frac{1}{12}x^3$

6. $\frac{1}{5}x^5 - \frac{2}{3}x^3 + \frac{5}{2}x^2 + c$ **7.** $c + 2x + \frac{1}{2}x^2 - \frac{2}{3}x^3 - \frac{1}{4}x^4$

8. $\frac{7}{2}x^2 + 3x + c$ **9.** $x^4 - 4x^3 + c$ **10.** $\frac{1}{3}x^3 + \dfrac{3}{x} + c$

11. $4x^3 + 2$ **12.** -4

13. $y = x^3 - 5x^2 + 3$; $(-\frac{2}{3}, \frac{13}{27})$, $(4, -13)$

14. $y = x^2 - 6x + 8$; $(2, 0)$, $(4, 0)$

15. $y = 2x^3 - 3x^2 + 4$; $(-1, -1)$

Exercise 28 (page 41)

1. $6\frac{1}{3}$ **2.** $\frac{3}{4}$ **3.** 12   **4.** -2

5. $16\frac{1}{2}$ **6.** $6a^2$ **7.** 42   **8.** $4\frac{1}{4}$

9. $4\frac{1}{2}$ **10.** $\frac{1}{6}$ **11.** $10\frac{2}{3}$ **12.** $5\frac{1}{2}$

13. $6\frac{1}{5}\pi$ **14.** $\frac{2}{3}\pi$ **15.** 56π **16.** $7\frac{1}{3}\pi$

17. $\frac{1}{30}\pi$ **18.** $17\frac{1}{15}\pi$; $203 : 53$

EXERCISE 29 (page 42)

1. 5, 20   **2.** 10, 22   **3.** 3, 59   **4.** $2t^2 + 3t$

5. $t^3 - 2t^2 + 3t$ **6.** 80 m, 53 m

7. 19 m/s, $1\frac{1}{2}$ s, $13\frac{1}{2}$ m   **8.** $\frac{3}{4}$; 8, 48, 12

9. Increasing at 40 cm³/min, decreasing at 20 cm³/min

10. $-900/v^2$ **11.** $2\pi r^2 + 12\pi r$; 24π

12. 9 m/s², $20\frac{1}{4}$ m/s, 9 s, $121\frac{1}{2}$ m

13. $(4t - 3t^2 + 15)$ m/s, $(15t + 2t^2 - t^3)$ m, 40 m/s

14. 136 m/s; 8 m, 280 m; 17 m/s², 41 m/s²

EXERCISE 30 (page 44)

7. 15   **8.** 42   **9.** 52   **10.** 128

11. 45°, 30°, 18°   **12.** 144°, 140°, $157\frac{1}{2}$°

13. Yes, 9; No; Yes, 36; No; Yes, 15

14. Yes, 18; Yes, 30; No; Yes, 16

15. 148°   **16.** 93   **17.** 36°, 72°, 72°; 72°

18. 8, 9   **19.** 84°   **20.** 45°, 72°

21. 15°, 15°, 150°

EXERCISE 31 (page 47)

1. (i) HIJ, PQR   (ii) LMN, STV, XYZ

2. (*a*) AB = QR, AC = PR   (*b*) GH, DF, EF/GJ

7. BDH, ADC, BEC, AEH; DC, EC, EH; $4\frac{1}{2}$ cm, $1\frac{2}{3}$ cm

8. AEB, CED; AE = $4\frac{2}{3}$ cm, ED = $7\frac{1}{2}$ cm

9. ADF and AEB, ACB and FDB, ACD and EBD; BE = $4\frac{1}{2}$ cm, DE = $3\frac{1}{2}$ cm, DF = 3 cm

Exercise 32 (page 48)

5. Rectangle; isosceles trapezium; parallelogram; kite; rhombus; square
6. Rectangle; rhombus; square

Exercise 33 (page 50)

1. 2.8 cm

Exercise 34 (page 51)

1. 6.94 cm	2. 5.51 cm	3. 6.30, 7.56, 7.09 cm	
4. 3.78 cm	5. 3.78 cm	8. 5.6 cm	9. 5.20 cm
10. 3.57 cm			

Exercise 35 (page 52)

1. 4.25 cm   2. 22° 37′   3. 2.82 cm   4. 5.03 cm
5. 42° 50′   6. 181 m   7. 1.06 cm   8. 67° 23′
9. 5.26 cm   10. 106° 16′   11. S. 63° 26′ E.
12. 0.8699, 0.4931   13. 0.2800   14. 72° 38′
15. 102° 41′   16. 36° 52′, 19° 27′
17. 10.4 cm   18. 7.10 cm   19. 1.49; 29° 11′
20. 2.12 cm, 1.54 cm   21. 10.5 cm, 9.66 cm, 309 cm²
22. 2.74 cm, 7.52 cm   23. 3.4 m
24. 1.36 m, 2.29 m
25. 10 cm, 81° 17′, 97° 33′, 91° 10′
26. 16.3 km, N. 27° 31′ E.   27. 38 m, 32 m
28. 43.9 km, 57.2(5) km   29. 1.72 cm, 5.44 cm
30. 15.2 cm

EXERCISE 36 (page 54)

1. 36 cm², 7.2 cm   **2.** 4.8 cm, 4 cm

3. 22.3 cm²   **4.** 87.6 cm²   **5.** 40° 54′, 139° 6′

6. 30°   **7.** 27.0 cm²   **8.** 25.7 cm²

9. 17.1 cm², 85.6 cm²   **10.** $22\frac{1}{2}$ cm²

11. 12 cm²   **12.** $\frac{1}{4}$ **13.** 28 cm², 12 cm²

14. $\frac{2}{3}, \frac{1}{2}, \frac{5}{6}$ **15.** $18x$ cm²

EXERCISE 37 (page 56)

1. 8.98 cm   **2.** 5.3 cm   **3.** 5.2 cm

5. $48\frac{1}{2}°$ **6.** 9.42 cm   **7.** 4.84 cm

EXERCISE 38 (page 57)

1. 0.9511, −0.8192, −1.4826, 0.4337, −0.1507, −0.2524, −0.7919, −0.3787

2. 63° or 117°, 34° 42′ or 145° 18′, 57° 36′, 122° 24′, 142° 45′, 110° 35′, 33° 49′, 163° 4′

3. 0.8988, −2.0503   **4.** 0.4226, −0.6428

5. 2.8239, −0.8098   **6.** −2.8239, 1.4150

7. 0.6018, −0.9336

8. 26°, 34°; −0.2419, −0.7193; −1.1918, −0.1763

9. 4.11 cm²   **10.** 30° or 150°

EXERCISE 39 (page 58)

1. 5.00   **2.** 8.52   **3.** 62.0   **4.** 419

5. 14.2   **6.** 2.63   **7.** 37.8(5)   **8.** 23.0

9. 14.1   **10.** 10.3(5), 7.23, 44°   **11.** 329, 134, 20°

12. 4.08, 3.66(5), 53° 24′   **13.** 113 m, 109 m

14. 8.95 nautical miles; $2.14\frac{1}{2}$ p.m.

15. 111 m, 36 m   **16.** 5.04 km, 5.56 km

17. 12.49.6 p.m., 258 km

Exercise 40 (page 59)

1. 10; 13; 37 **2.** 15; 12; 56 **3.** 13.6; 16.6

4. 7 **5.** 7.07 cm **6.** 15 cm, 120 cm²

7. 2.8 cm **8.** 12.5 cm **9.** 6.08 cm

11. $\sqrt{208}$ cm, $\sqrt{325}$ cm, $\sqrt{533}$ cm **12.** 6 cm

14. 90 cm, 73° 44' **15.** $\sqrt{(4x^2 - y^2)}$

24. $\frac{4}{5}$, $\frac{4}{3}$ **25.** $-\frac{15}{17}$, $-\frac{8}{15}$ **26.** $\frac{24}{25}$, $-\frac{24}{7}$

27. 3 **28.** $\frac{5}{9}$, $\frac{9}{4}$ **29.** $\frac{20}{29}$, $\frac{21}{29}$, $-\frac{20}{29}$

30. P + Q = 90°; P $\sim$ Q = 90°

31. $\dfrac{1}{\sqrt{2}}$, $\dfrac{1}{\sqrt{2}}$, $-\dfrac{1}{\sqrt{2}}$; $\dfrac{\sqrt{3}}{2}$, $-\frac{1}{2}$, $-\sqrt{3}$; $\frac{1}{2}$, $\frac{1}{2}$, $-\dfrac{1}{\sqrt{3}}$

32. 60°; 120°; 45°; 60° or 120° **33.** $\frac{1}{4}$; $\frac{1}{2}$

34. $\sin^2\theta$; $2 + 3\sin^2\theta$ **35.** $\frac{1}{2}$; 2

36. $\frac{1}{2}$; $\dfrac{\sqrt{3}}{4}$; $\frac{3}{2}$ **37.** 1; $\sqrt{6}$; $\frac{1}{3}$; 2

38. 60° or 120°; 30° or 150° **39.** 7 cm, 7$\sqrt{3}$ cm

40. 10 cm, 10$\sqrt{3}$ cm

Exercise 41 (page 62)

1. 4.34 **2.** 12.5 **3.** 16.8 **4.** 41° 24'/25'

5. 111° 48' **6.** 58° 40', 41° 4', 80° 16'

7. 15.6, 29° 4', 41° 56' **8.** 28° 10', 119° 15', 32° 35'

9. 120° **10.** 7.05 cm, 14.91 cm

11. 14.5 km, 193° 21' **12.** $-\frac{1}{4}$, 8 cm

13. 7 cm, 4.36 cm, 58° 23' **15.** 224 m, 165 m, 159 m

Exercise 42 (page 63)

1. 12 cm; 7.14 cm **2.** 6.4 or 1.4 cm **3.** 19°

4. 57° **5.** 12 cm; 6.5 cm **6.** 9 cm

7. 4 cm, 1.8 cm, 4.8 cm

Exercise 43 (page 65)

1. 50°, 130°, 25°   **2.** 46°, 104°

3. $(90 - x)°$, $(90 + x)°$ **4.** 28°, 34°, 118°, 90°, 62°

5. 32°, 48°, 96°   **6.** 85°, 52°   **7.** 68°, 13°

8. $3x°$ **9.** $180 - \frac{1}{2}y$; 120   **10.** 128°, 116°

Exercise 45 (page 68)

1. 55°, 20°   **2.** 84°   **3.** 66°   **4.** 56°, 84°, 40°

5. 70°, 75°   **6.** 132°, 104°   **12.** 36°

Exercise 46 (page 69)

1. 4.14 cm, 1.94 cm   **2.** 7.66 cm, 8.66 cm, 9.40 cm

3. 6.32 cm, 7.14 cm, 7.76 cm   **4.** 3.32 cm, 3.10 cm

5. 67° 8′   **6.** 8.93 cm

7. 5.11 cm, 2.42 cm   **9.** 3.32 cm

Exercise 47 (page 71)

1. 4.2, 7.2   **2.** 3, 6, 4, 4   **3.** $2\frac{1}{2}$ **4.** 6, 6

5. 12.2 m, $\dfrac{x^2 + y^2}{2x}$ **8.** AH . HD; BD . BC; CE . CA

Exercise 48 (page 73)

1. 5, 10, 6, 8   **2.** 5 cm, $3\frac{3}{4}$ cm, $2\frac{1}{4}$ cm

3. 12 cm, 6 cm   **4.** DCY, ADX, DBX; 1 : 3, 7 : 2, 7 : 3

5. 14.4 cm, 9.6 cm   **6.** 7 : 8

7. 3.56 cm, 4.44 cm; 8.4 cm, 2.4 cm   **14.** No

EXERCISE 49 (page 74)

1. $1 : 4$, $\quad 4 : 9$, $\quad 9 : 16$ **2.** $3 : 8$, $\quad 3 : 5$, $\quad 9 : 25$

3. $3 : 5$, $\quad 9 : 25$, $\quad 27 : 125$ **4.** 11; $\quad 9 : 16$; $\quad 4 : 1$; $\quad 3 : 8$

5. $2\frac{1}{4}$ cm, $3\frac{3}{4}$ cm; $5\frac{1}{3}$ cm², 12 cm², $31\frac{2}{3}$ cm²

6. $\frac{1}{8}$, $\frac{1}{12}$, $\frac{5}{12}$

EXERCISE 50 (page 76)

1. $7\frac{1}{2}$, $17\frac{1}{2}$, $90°$, 5 **2.** 5, 21

3. 24, 216, 115.2 **4.** 6, $\quad 2 : 1$

EXERCISE 51 (page 77)

2. 5.74 cm   **3.** 4.06 cm

EXERCISE 52 (page 79)

1. 202 m; 43 m; $4° 33'$ **2.** $9° 39'$, $15° 50'$

3. 13.8 cm, $40° 16'$ **4.** 19.0 cm; 12.2 cm; $37°42'$

5. 6.84 cm, 17.10 cm, $8° 48'$ **6.** 11.2 m; 39 m

EXERCISE 53 (page 80)

1. $\frac{5}{6}$, $\frac{6}{5}$; $\frac{1}{2}$; $\frac{3}{4}$; $\dfrac{8}{\sqrt{61}}$

2. $79° 36'$; $14° 22'$; $30° 31'$; $51° 54'$

3. $54° 44'$; $35° 16'$; $70° 32'$

4. $56° 15'$; $67° 30'$; $61° 52'$ or $53'$; $56° 15'$; $43° 41'$

5. $53° 8'$; $62° 37'$

6. 3.46 cm; 5.20 cm; 4.90 cm; $70° 32'$; $54° 44'$

Exercise 54 (page 81)

5. 25°   **6.** 26½°, 35°   **7.** 58°, 66°

8. 2.2/3 cm, 3.6 cm   **9.** 6.6 cm   **10.** 71°, 65°

Exercise 55 (page 82)

1. 1 : 25 344, 1 : 100 000   **2.** 2.85 km, 16 mm

3. $\frac{1}{7}$ **4.** 290 m

5. 10 m/s, 300°   **6.** 22.5 km/h, 066°

7. 468 km/h, 274°   **8.** 673 km/h, 025°

9. 71.6 km/h, 216°   **10.** 107 km/h, 135°

11. 8°, 375 km/h   **12.** 10°, 355 km/h

13. 3.47 knots, 6.43 nautical miles

14. 2.47 knots, 7° 36½' N. of E.

15. 172°, 424 km/h, 45 min   **16.** 90 km/h, 312°

17. 040°, 587 km/h   **18.** 051°, 129°; 66 min, 43 min

Exercise 56 (page 84)

1. 4.19   **2.** 76° 24'   **3.** 12.9   **4.** 14.4

5. 20.1   **6.** 5.33(5)   **7.** 4⅙ cm, 49° 15', 9.09 cm

8. 276°   **9.** 9451 km   **10.** 4095 km   **11.** 5361 km

12. 5560 km   **13.** 4986 km   **14.** 46° 4', 5122 km

15. 62° 11' N. or S.   **16.** 933 km   **17.** 9 h 45 min

18. 21° 12' S.   **19.** 1936 km   **20.** 8° 20'

21. 48° 14'   **22.** 3650 km; 6630 km; 62° 39'; 6970 km

23. 11 870 km

Paper I (page 87)

1. 0.72; 0.4375, 0.076; 70 cm

2. $(3a + 2b)(3a - 2b)$, $4(2x + 1)(x - 1)$; $\sqrt{\dfrac{y - q}{p}}$; 4, $-2\frac{1}{2}$

3. $\frac{1}{4}$, $-\sqrt{3}$, 10°; 12 cm, 73° 44', 143° 8', 108 cm²

5. £33.90; 122 cm³   **6.** 58 m, 59° 42'

PAPER 2 (page 88)

1. $\frac{1}{7}$; £12.60; $\frac{8}{17}$, $-\frac{15}{17}$

2. $15p$; $\dfrac{1}{y(y+1)}$; 6

3. 10, 54°; $1\frac{5}{6}$ cm, $4\frac{4}{5}$ cm

4. (1, 4), (3, 0), $6\frac{3}{4}$ **5.** 31.5 mm

6. 8, 4, 12; 1668 km/h, 60° 30'

PAPER 3 (page 89)

1. 0.15; 3.5 cm, 0.105, 0.598   **2.** -2; 1, $\frac{2}{3}$; 6.55

3. $3\frac{3}{4}$, $3\frac{1}{3}$, $1\frac{11}{21}$ **4.** 2.7, 26° 3'

5. 28, $489\frac{3}{5}\pi$ **6.** £12.50, £12, 125

PAPER 4 (page 90)

1. 8.53; 38m²; £2

2. $(3x+7y)(2x-3y)$, $(x+5)(y-4)$; $10x^4 + 8x - \dfrac{12}{x^3}$,

     $\frac{1}{2}x^4 + 3x - \dfrac{4}{x} + c$; $\sqrt[4]{\left(\dfrac{188^2 EI}{N^2 w}\right)}$, 8.94

3. 7.04 cm, 26.9 cm²   **4.** $(8x - \frac{1}{2}x^2)$ cm², 3.31

6. 460 km/h, 304°; 217°

PAPER 5 (page 91)

1. 5.6 km/h; $41\frac{2}{3}$%; 43.8 cm²

2. $\dfrac{2(s-ut)}{t^2}$; $\dfrac{x^2-2}{(x-3)(x+1)(x+2)}$; -0.85, 1.65

3. 28°, 20°, 132°   **4.** 7.02 cm; 73° 17'; 8.35 cm

5. 44 km/h

6. 18 m/s; 24 s, 288 m; 36 s, 54 m/s; 8 s, 16 s